# Technical

# COMMUNICATION

**A Pocket Guide**

Joanne Buckley

Lawrence Gulston
*Sir Sandford Fleming College*

**NELSON** EDUCATION

# NELSON EDUCATION

**Technical Communication: A Pocket Guide**
by Joanne Buckley and Lawrence Gulston

**Associate Vice President, Editorial Director:**
Evelyn Veitch

**Editor-in-Chief, Higher Education:**
Anne Williams

**Acquisitions Editor:**
Bram Sepers

**Marketing Manager:**
Amanda Henry

**Developmental Editor:**
My Editor Inc.

**Permissions Coordinator:**
Shelley Wickabrod

**Senior Content Production Manager:**
Anne Nellis

**Production Service:**
Graphic World Inc.

**Copy Editor:**
Kate Revington

**Proofreader:**
Graphic World Inc.

**Indexer:**
Graphic World Inc.

**Production Coordinator:**
Ferial Suleman

**Design Director:**
Ken Phipps

**Managing Designer:**
Katherine Strain

**Interior Design:**
Peter Papayanakis

**Cover Design:**
Peter Papayanakis

**Cover Image:**
© iStockphoto.com/Pawel Kaminski

**Compositor:**
Graphic World Inc.

**Printer:**
Webcom

**Library and Archives Canada Cataloguing in Publication**

Buckley, Joanne, 1953-

Technical communication : a pocket guide / Joanne Buckley, Lawrence Gulston. -- 1st ed.

Includes Index.
ISBN 978-0-17-644091-6

1. Technical writing.
2. Communication of technical information.

I. Gulston, Lawrence II. Title

T11.B82 2009    808'.0666
C2008-907062-3

ISBN-13: 978-0-17-644091-6
ISBN-10: 0-17-644091-7

# BRIEF TABLE OF CONTENTS

# TABLE OF CONTENTS

# INTRODUCTION

*Technical Communication: A Pocket Guide* will help you to concise answers to common questions that technical writers ask while preparing documents and other presentations of technical information. The pocket format makes it handy for students going off to class or for working engineers heading into the field with laptops.

In this compact book, the technical writer will find all that is necessary to answer questions that naturally arise while writing according to a recursive writing process, working with the English language, and determining how to document secondary source materials in an appropriate style (CSE or IEEE).

Chapters 1 to 5 outline and explain the writing process as the technical writer experiences it: establishing audience and purpose, gathering research materials, organizing the research into a coherent plan, writing several drafts that include graphic presentations of data, and documenting materials borrowed from published sources. Each part of the writing process is explained clearly with specific examples to illustrate, and each of these chapters ends with a checklist to review before going on to the next stage in writing a document.

Chapters 6 to 9 explain and illustrate language issues faced by the technical writer: they address grammar, style, punctuation, and mechanics. Each chapter explains the most common faults and shows how to correct them. Grammar is the way an English sentence is put together. Style is how to use the language to express one's ideas and information so that the reader can most quickly and clearly understand them. Punctuation is the system used to mark off grammatical units in a sentence to make meaning clearer. Mechanics refers to some of the specialized issues of technical writing: capitalization; the use of numbers, abbreviations, and hyphenation; scientific notation; and the format for mathematical equations and formulae.

Chapters 10 and 11 outline the documentation systems set out for writers in technical professions by the Council of Science Editors (CSE) and the Institute of Electrical and Electronic Engineers (IEEE). The book ends with a glossary of usage, an alphabetical list of English words commonly misunderstood and misused.

# ACKNOWLEDGMENTS

Thanks must first go to Joanne Buckley, whose lucid *Checkmate* text formed the basis of the sections on grammar, punctuation, mechanics, and usage. For their invaluable comments and suggestions about the manuscript, my gratitude extends to Barb Graham, *St. Clair College*; Ryan Gibbs, *Lambton College*; and Robert Ritchie, *Fanshawe College*. I also acknowledge and thank Katherine Goodes at My Editor, for her kind patience and proficiency in the role of developmental editor, and Kate Revington, for her passionate copy editing that tightened and brightened the text. Thanks, too, go to Bram Sepers and the folks at Nelson for seeing the project through.

This book is dedicated to Deborah Luchuk, my dear heart and inspiration.

*Lawrie Gulston*

# AUDIENCE AND PURPOSE

**1**

As a technical communicator, you have a particular kind of story to tell, but you share the same goals as most writers:

- to get your reader's attention
- to build the narrative with new and interesting detail
- to keep it short—the right number of words and no more
- to study what good writers of your type do, analyze their work, and apply what you learn in your own writing
- to connect with others of like mind and help them with your knowledge

## LANGUAGE AND THE TECHNICAL WRITER

### LANGUAGE MATTERS

Language matters. A technical communication handbook like this is addressed to an audience of professionals who are focused on and passionate about their scientific and technical work, not about language. Indeed, they often find the natural intricacies and inconsistencies of language bewildering and frustrating.

For example, language is often ambiguous. Words and phrases can carry two or more meanings at the same time. Does *two hundred litre containers* mean two containers of one hundred litres each, or an unspecified number of containers of two hundred litres each?

### THE DIMENSIONS OF LANGUAGE

It isn't surprising, then, that written language can become a problem for the technical writer. There is no face-to-face or voice communication providing feedback, no instant correction of an error. The written technical language must be as direct, complete, correct, and precise as humanly possible before being placed in a channel of communication for transmission to the intended reader.

Context is one important dimension of language of which the writer must be continually aware. The specific meaning that your audience will take from your words depends, in part, on the context—the words, phrases, and sentences—that surrounds a word or phrase and suggests which meaning is intended. To make intended meaning clear, then, the technical writer must often add specific context: explanations, definitions, analogies, graphic presentations, and the like. Sometimes, it just takes knowledge of the conventions of punctuation: *two hundred-litre containers*.

Ambiguity, often found in general speech, is another dimension of language which often appears in a written draft. A *chalk line*, for example, could refer to an instrument for marking a straight line or to the line itself. *Dirt* could refer to any substance that soils fabric or specifically to soil, the product of earth crustal processes in which we grow plants. To reduce such ambiguity, technical professionals prefer to use the technical language appropriate to their disciplines, each technical term tending to have only one, specific meaning. Part of technical training and experience is learning such terms and learning to use them precisely and appropriately.

However, the highly specialized vocabulary of technical professionals can isolate their communication from a more general audience. The starting point for each piece of technical communication, then, must include a consideration of how much technical vocabulary the intended audience can understand.

Taking a broad and balanced view of the dimensions of language is a useful strategy in a technical profession. Most technical writers acknowledge the need to write technical documents clearly and concisely. Communicating well requires time and expertise, and technical communication requires even more of these. To be useful to a technical audience, your information must be understood easily so that it can be acted upon appropriately.

## A TOOL IN DEVELOPING NEW TECHNOLOGIES

Writing clearly about technology has other implications besides the dissemination of technical information. Written language is a powerful tool in the process of designing and developing new technologies. Language can shape the thinking of engineers, designers, and technologists and lead them to invent new products and new solutions to old problems. Technical communication is the primary means of documenting processes, procedures, and specifications after something has been built. It is the means of marketing technical products to specific audiences.

Language matters and deserves a prominent place in the thinking of those who create and write about technology.

## ◼ THE WRITING PROCESS

The key to producing a sound technical document is a sound writing process. When creating documents, successful technical writers take their work through a recursive five-stage process with these components:

1. identifying required information, based on intended audience and purpose
2. researching the required information thoroughly in reliable sources
3. organizing the research with an outline
4. drafting the research into sentences, paragraphs, and sections, using the outline as a guide
5. revising and editing the text to meet the needs of the intended audience and to achieve the defined purpose in writing

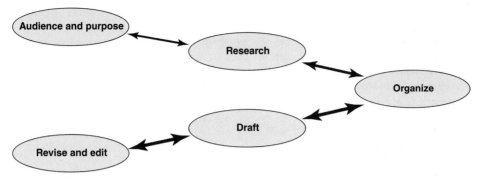

**Figure 1.1** The Writing Process

The writing process is both linear and recursive. Following the process above as a sequence of steps will produce a document with complete information expressed in a clearly expressed and well-organized manner; however, each step can never be absolutely finished before going on to the next step. Human error and changing circumstances will demand changes as the writer progresses, making it necessary to revisit previous stages in the process.

The writer's eye is never quiet. As you work through the stages illustrated below, you will continually review and check previous stages, make content changes, and balance the elements of your writing to connect with your intended audience. For example, as you read through a late draft for grammar and spelling errors, it may occur to you that a paragraph contains statements that need verification from an outside source. So you would go back to the research stage and look further for published material to corroborate your statements. The paragraph is then rewritten, revised, and re-edited.

This recursive process is normal. It may seem messy to one accustomed to following a linear procedure toward a testable conclusion, but it is an inevitable part of writing and yields a better product.

Plan what you think is enough time to cover all the stages of the writing process. Be sure to budget more time yet for recursive writing activities.

## ANALYZING THE WRITING TASK

The first step in planning any written document is deciding what is required. Accurate assessment of the type and scope of information and the expected formatting of the communication will ensure that you satisfy your audience's expectations and achieve your own goals in communicating. Anything else is a waste of your time and effort. Consider these questions:

- Why am I writing this?
- What length of document is appropriate in this situation?
- In what form should I transmit the information?

## KNOWING YOUR AUDIENCE

Meeting the needs of your audience is essential to a successful communication. All good writing decisions about what to say and how to say it are based on efforts to meet the needs of a specific audience.

- Is your audience an individual, perhaps your supervisor, or a group of technical professionals, a committee, or a general audience of end users of a product?

- What essentials about this subject does the audience need to know? What do they already know about this topic?
- What, if any, communication have you had from the audience?
- What is the best channel of communication to use with this audience?
- What level of language will the audience understand most easily? How will they expect the information to be organized?

We do not write technical texts for ourselves; we write for an interested audience that intends to use the information we present for their own practical purposes.

## RESPECT YOUR AUDIENCE

Having a firm sense of audience is not exclusive to technical communication—any effective communication will be designed for those who will receive it and will respect their needs and concerns. Yet scientists and technicians typically focus on the content of a communication, on the technical process and problems they have to overcome, and as a result, tend to overlook the needs of their audiences. The first rule of technical communication is "Respect your audience."

An example of how this rule is commonly violated is the use of technical language, or jargon. Technicians and engineers live in specialized worlds with specialized languages, and they use these languages to seek out and identify others who share their world and to convey precise meaning around technical situations, problems, and solutions at meetings or on the factory floor. To an outsider, however, this specialized language of short forms and acronyms is bewildering.

One should also not assume that the reader knows the science, technology, or engineering principles that underlie the discussion at hand. Never assume.

How we think is directly related to how we write. If we focus our thinking solely on technical problems and solutions, our writing will tend to be less accessible and usable to the reader unfamiliar with our profession or field. To be useful, technology must be shared. If you are in business and do not take that approach, you risk losing customers and revenue.

Being aware of your audience's needs and characteristics, while essential, is not as easy as it sounds, even when you know the intended audience personally. Technical writers need to ask themselves good questions: Why did we do this project? Who benefits? How does this information help the reader? Is this confusing? The answers to these questions will greatly improve connections with the intended audience. We can, however, identify some types of readers and their concerns that the technical writer will most often find in the workplace.

## SUPERVISORS

Supervisors manage projects and people. They may not be familiar with the specific technologies or the specific subject you are writing about, so you must explain specific concepts, procedures, and technical details clearly and thoroughly so that they cannot be misunderstood. Supervisors usually do not need complete detail because they will not be performing procedures. Their first concerns will be time and money spent on the project, and the results of the project—the goals achieved with the outlay of resources.

This audience is usually a person you know, and thus you can call or e-mail to get a clear idea of that person's specific needs regarding the content and format of your document, as well as the purpose of the communication.

A supervisor may wish to pass your document on to others for specific reasons. Sales staff, for example, may need to know about a new product you developed. A safety committee may need to know about potential dangers inherent in a new procedure you have developed. As you select content for your document, keep these secondary audiences in mind. They may require more detail, more explanation, a simplified diagram, and so on.

Supervisors are often familiar with theoretical science. Writing for this expert audience, you can use longer sentences and technical terminology without having to translate ideas into simpler terms.

## TECHNICIANS

Repair and maintenance manuals, for example, are written for working technicians. This audience needs to act on your information, so the writing must be accurate and well supported by appropriate graphic presentations: graphs, charts, diagrams, exploded views, colour photos, and so on.

Most writing for technicians assumes that the reader has some training and experience so that explanations of theory, basic procedures, and common tools or equipment, such as a digital multimeter, will not be needed. The technician needs lists of parts, equipment, and safe steps in a procedure. Keep language simple: use short sentences and common vocabulary.

## PROFESSIONAL RESEARCHERS

Scientific papers and research reports are written for a science audience involved in research. These papers and reports should follow accepted methods of describing research goals and methodologies and present research results with a discussion and analysis. A longer average sentence length and scientific vocabulary can be part of such reports.

## CLIENTS

Those who buy and use technical products, such as electronic instruments for surveying or chemical analysis, are sometimes called "users" in owners' manuals. A better choice would be "client" or "customer." A person who wants to buy an instrument or a group representing a company interested in buying your technologies wants to feel that their needs have been understood before deciding to purchase. The manuals you write should reflect those needs.

Language is a competitive advantage. Consider a federal government contract to survey the proposed route of an oil pipeline in the Mackenzie Delta. Several surveying companies will bid on the same contract. The winning proposal will likely provide the clearest description of technical problems and their solutions, as well as a competitive price. It will be written in plain English that non-surveyors can read and understand easily.

## ▌ IDENTIFYING YOUR PURPOSE

Knowing your purpose is also essential. Together, identifying your audience and purpose is the best way to set your writing goals and answer all the questions of content and format that come up as you write.

Ask yourself these sorts of questions:

- What will this audience likely do with the document?
- Why does the audience need this information?
- Shall I make recommendations, based on this information?
- Do I need to describe the step-by-step assembly procedure for this audience?
- Shall I describe only the best-selling features of this new product for a potential target market?

Most technical communication is created to inform or to persuade the audience. The expectations of your audience are part of this decision. Does your boss expect a factual report, or should you include a set of recommendations that advocate a specific course of action? Each audience has its own need for information.

You have your own need to write. Writing is part of a technical professional's work. Many are involved in technical work, but only a few take time to write well. A well-written document will promote your career.

- Requests for equipment, for grant money, or for project approval are routine, but to be successful, they must be written persuasively.
- Briefing documents for your supervisor allow technical information to flow upwards in an organization and produce better corporate decisions.
- Technical articles in journals or technical papers read at conferences make you known to wider audiences and help you to network and to increase your opportunities for collaborative projects.
- A well-written manual can raise your profile within your industry and make you money as well.

## REPORT TYPES BY PURPOSE

Scientific and technical reports can be classified by their intended purpose. Knowing your audience and purpose has implications for the organizational plans of workplace documents, which have to meet audience expectations and fulfill a specific purpose by following a conventional pattern of content development. Some examples of typical report patterns follow.

- Scientific papers
  - Purpose: primary and secondary goals of the research
  - Review of Literature: summary and evaluation of published work
  - Methods: methodology used and any variation required in standard methods
  - Results: usually with graphics to summarize data in a compact form
  - Discussion: analysis of results with graphics to show trends, structures, functions, and so on

- Progress reports
  - Introduction: scope and purpose of the project
  - Work Completed: tasks completed in reporting period
  - Work Remaining: task planned for next reporting period
  - Problems and Adjustments: when required by circumstance
  - Conclusion: summarize and evaluate work to date and planned

- Field trip reports
  - Introduction: aims, methods, study area (with map), background data
  - Activities: organized by type under descriptive headings
  - Conclusion: summary, results, appendix with field data sheets

- Incident reports
  - Introduction: purpose, scope, background
  - Investigation: facts of the incident
  - Causes: inferences about possible causes
  - Results: consequences (losses, delays, injuries, and so on)
  - Recommendations: practical suggestions

- Proposals
  - Executive Summary

- Introduction: purpose and scope of planned work
- Proposal Plan: planned work (factual, detailed, practical)
- Qualifications: company projects, resumés of personnel
- Scope and Methodology: overview of task, current technologies
- Facilities, Personnel, Duration
- Budget: set realistic goals
- Reports and Benefits: frequency of reports to client, benefits to client

- Feasibility Studies
  - Purpose and Scope of the Study
  - Methodology: how the investigation was done
  - Results of the Investigation
  - Discussion: summary and analysis of significant findings
  - Recommendations

# ▉ INFORMATION SOURCING

Identify the types of sources you will use to create your document. Primary sources of information are those you generate from field or lab experimentation, from first-hand observation and data recording. Secondary sources are those published in standard texts, in professional journals, and on the Internet. Use these to provide useful examples or to compare and corroborate your own findings.

Knowing which secondary sources of information are authoritative and generally considered appropriate for your audience and purpose will help you assemble the best and most reliable information.

## DOCUMENT FORMATTING

Knowing the specific format requirements of your document is another essential piece of the planning puzzle. Generally, the longer your document, the more formal it will be, and the more pieces of front and back matter you will need. Consider these questions:

- Which is more appropriate: an e-mail or a written memo?
- What parts of a formal report—for example, a letter of transmittal, an informative abstract, or a glossary—will you need?
- What type of document are you creating: a proposal, a feasibility study, or a lab report? Each type has its own typical content and structure.
- What style of documentation will you use: CSE name-year, CSE citation-sequence, or IEEE? (See Chapters 10 and 11.) This decision will determine how to record the sources of information that you select for your document drafts.
- What will be the length of the completed report? The most accurate assessment of the length of a piece of writing is a word count. This length can be negotiated with the person requesting the document, or you can focus on the content and write as much as needed to inform your reader clearly and concisely. An executive typically wants the shortest possible explanation. A technical professional wants a detailed, step-by-step procedure to follow. A scientist wants a thorough discussion of all possible causes.

Short reports are typically sent as e-mails, the electronic equivalent of a two-page memo. Technical communications in e-mail format can include graphics, such as charts or digital images; the sections of content can be identified under descriptive headings. Note that the heading enhancements in the sample e-mail below are text based; the use of HTML e-mail with colour, boldface, and other enhancements is not widespread in business and industry.

To:       A.S. Rogers
From:    John McLean
Subject:  Product TS40X—Modifications
Date:    30 November 2009
Hi Al,

As requested, I'm reporting for the product group on this project. The planned modifications to the TS40X were completed on Monday and tested yesterday with the following results.

*Headgear Assembly*
- Rotation speed: 1560 rpm
- Torque: 45 ft/lb
- Range of motion: 75°
- Stress loading: 45% over spec

INSPECTION REVEALED NO WEAR OR DAMAGE FROM OVERLOAD TESTING.

*Trigger Unit*
CMOS device: adjusted to 1120 kb/sec to maximize efficiency
Trigger Rates: 14 000—55 000 events/sec
Reed Switch: 15 mA circuit and servo installed; tested OK

*Summary*
The product group is satisfied with the modifications and recommends moving into production next week.

Regards,
John

# CHECKLIST FOR AUDIENCE AND PURPOSE

Before you begin your writing project, have you

- set your writing goals?
- assessed the level of technical language appropriate for your audience?
- noted any problematic tendencies with language (e.g., spelling, vague language)?
- planned adequate time for the writing process?
- determined the type and scope of information?
- determined the expected formatting of the communication?
- assessed accurately your audience's needs and level of knowledge?
- clarified your supervisor's needs in this communication?
- provided enough detail for a technical audience?
- considered the client's needs in an owners' manual?
- identified the specific purpose of this communication?
- identified the type of report you require according to its purpose?
- identified the types of sources of information you will need?
- identified the length, format, type, and style of documentation required?

# 2

# RESEARCHING YOUR INFORMATION

Collecting, assessing, and selecting information for your audience are essential to good technical communication because readers want detailed, accurate facts. In a sense, a technical writer is a reporter, gathering details of a process or steps in a procedure.

Through research, you can ensure that the required detail is there. Research takes persistence; it means not giving up when your effort seems to produce nothing. Remember that each disappointment leads you a step closer to the information you need. Your research must be solid because your audience values accurate, dependable data. Details are the stuff of good technical communication and cannot easily be edited in later.

## BEFORE YOU BEGIN

Develop clear, achievable goals for research by first assessing your audience's needs and your purpose for writing. Time spent selecting research goals and planning your research strategies will help you to avoid wasting time collecting unusable material. Strategies for gathering information are a product of your experience and training, your knowledge of the subject and sources of information on that subject, and your understanding of writing principles.

Thorough research ensures that your work in the next stages in the writing process will be efficient and effective. Any problem in the writing process will affect the stages that follow. If your research notes cannot be organized easily, take a step back and look at your audience and purpose again.

Students especially will likely need to begin the research process with an overview of the subject in order to identify specific types of information required and likely sources. An encyclopedia article or interview with an experienced colleague can provide such an overview. These sources do not appear in a References Cited list, but they provide the researcher with clear paths to worthwhile sources.

## BRAINSTORMING

Brainstorming is a process of identifying the most significant points you want to communicate and then finding creative ideas to link the points into a coherent narrative or to solve a central issue or problem. It involves writing down as much information as you can on the topic at hand and as many solutions to the central problem as you can think of.

Brainstorming can involve others working on the project with you or can be done alone. Different forms of individual brainstorming include free writing, word association, and diagramming—the latter involves using a web of lines to connect related ideas and information.

At this point, do not censor solutions. As you research and work through initial drafts, the best answers will become clear to you. Various methods of making decisions can be used to come to a conclusion.

For example, a group of engineers and technicians who need to use compressed air tools in residential neighbourhoods could brainstorm ideas to reduce the noise made by their tools.

Brainstorming your subject will help by showing you what you already know about the subject and pointing to what needs to be researched. The more specific the topics you are researching, the faster the research will be. It takes time to research a general subject and narrow it down to the specifics you need to write about.

## PRIORITIZING

Prioritize the information you will need into major and minor points so that you don't waste time on minor points. What information is central to your audience and purpose, and how much detail do you need? Find a method of identifying these all-important points in your research notes as you develop the information. Some writers use sticky notes with scribbled headings stuck to the relevant pages.

## IDENTIFYING INFORMATION SOURCES

Identify potential sources of information. Some are accessible more quickly than others, so maximize your research in a minimum of time. Remember to assess sources carefully. Many unreliable sources are accessible, but not seen as authoritative.

Begin research with sources that provide a good overview of your topic so that you can evaluate issues and identify further sources of more specific information. Sometimes, a veteran colleague working in the same field can help provide this overview.

## ALLOCATING RESEARCH TIME

Allocate adequate time for research. Do not underestimate how long it takes to do primary research or to seek out and assimilate needed information.

- Reading technical literature for comprehension takes more time than scanning a popular magazine article.
- Library books, videos, or journals listed in the catalogue may be checked out, so you may have to wait for information to be available.
- Questionnaires sent by mail can take weeks to return.
- Appointments for information interviews can be delayed or cancelled.
- Electronic forms of information are faster to process, but can produce quantities of irrelevant and inaccurate information that can mislead and frustrate an inexperienced researcher.

## DISTRIBUTING TECHNICAL INFORMATION

Scientific and technical information moves through a distribution process. First passed on informally through personal conversations and e-mails to colleagues, data can then be presented in a lecture, conference workshop, or journal article. These can be later incorporated into larger works, such as technical manuals, conference proceedings, casebooks, or textbooks.

Being aware of this process helps a researcher move through source materials more efficiently. The end products—textbooks and manuals—have more generalized, summary data; the originating products—journal articles and technical reports—have more specific and detailed information.

## WHAT GOOD RESEARCHERS HAVE

Good researchers have several characteristics in common:

- patience to follow every lead
- persistence to read sources thoroughly and retain useful information
- luck to find the right pieces, ones that give maximum value in minimum time

The information comes from two types of sources: personal experience as it is recorded—primary sources—and the published experience of others—secondary sources. A good technical communicator knows how to blend primary and secondary sources to create a coherent narrative and reach valid conclusions.

## ◼ PRIMARY RESEARCH

## THE VALUE OF PRIMARY RESEARCH

Raw data are the lifeblood of technical communication. Readers in the workplace need information about your discoveries, innovations, and solutions to technical problems. Recording and periodically writing up your work is essential to the flow of information in the workplace.

Primary research is science, a way to investigate the nature of phenomena. Writing about your investigations is an integral element of scientific and technical invention. Science, technology, and the practice of writing work together.

## EXPERIMENTATION

Research can be formal and extensive, or informal and brief to test specific hypotheses. In each case, primary research follows the same scientific method.

1. Define the question or problem.
2. Gather information and resources (e.g., equipment).
3. Form a specific hypothesis to test.
4. Carry out an experiment.
5. Observe results; collect the data.
6. Validate the data.
7. Interpret the data.
8. Report the results.

Standardized testing, such as the tests of the American Society for Testing and Materials for fuels and lubricants, provides standard methodologies that allow valid comparisons of test results across a series of experiments.

## NOTEBOOKS

Your most important primary source of information is your own field or lab journal. Learn how to take lab and field notes in college. It is a practical skill for the workplace.

The field notebook records primary data in hundreds of working situations: a tour of manufacturing facilities, a field trip to collect samples of minerals or benthic organisms, an inspection of monitoring equipment at a weather station, and so on.

Conducting experiments and making observations are essential in technical work. The field or lab notebook is often the only record brought back from the field or left after a lab experiment, the sole permanent record of your work and observations. Never leave things to memory.

Notebooks should meet the SCAN criteria: specific, complete, accurate, and neat. Collect all the specific detail that is pertinent to the purpose of your work.

In addition, record incidental observations that may help your interpretation of the data later. Record your own reflections, insights into the data, and any questions or speculations that might lead to further investigation.

## DATA SHEETS

Field or lab data sheets are designed so that detailed, relevant observations can be recorded. Use standardized tests and procedures so that recorded observations can be assessed accurately and valid comparisons made.

Modern electronic recorders capture information in digital form and permit downloading into a computer for analysis. In addition, bring basic field equipment into the field binoculars, sample bags, a digital camera, and a compass to broaden the scope of your observations. Many field crews now also carry laptop computers to speed the process of data analysis and reporting.

## INSTRUMENTATION

Primary data are most often collected from instrumentation in the field or laboratory.

Instruments can be simple mechanical devices, such as a compass or clinometer, or more complex electronic and electro-mechanical instruments: magnetometers, flow meters, GPS units, total stations, dumpy levels, seismometers, oscilloscopes, multimeters, bore hole loggers, and so on. Each of these instruments takes specific types of measurements that are displayed or recorded, most commonly now in a digital form.

Some instruments are designed to take samples in the field for analysis in a laboratory later. These include the diamond core drill for core sampling and the Kemmerer bottle for water sampling at depth. Some instruments, such as the gas chromatograph or mass spectrophotometer, are used in lab analysis.

Such instruments are designed for specific purposes and vary widely in their complexity. Learn the proper theory of operation, setup, calibration, safe operation, and maintenance of each that applies to you. Well-written user and technical manuals are essential to achieve good results with all instrumentation.

## PAPERWORK

Working with people involves working with paper.

You might find yourself working as part of a field crew, developing a proposal document with project engineers, or managing a project in the field.

In the process, you will receive many documents, either paper or in electronic form: memos, e-mails, invoices, data sheets from WHMIS (Workplace Hazardous Materials Information System), and so on. Keep copies of all project documents. They provide important, specific information that will contribute to the final writing project: a completion report, presentation to management, conference with project engineering staff, and so on.

# INTERVIEWS

Interviewing can provide you with detailed information from individuals who have expertise on your topic. Choose the style of interview appropriate for the availability of the individual you want to interview, your comfort level talking to people, and the technology you have available.

- *Face-to-face interviews* allow you to assess emotional reactions and to adapt your questions to the answers of the person you are interviewing. Ask to record the interview so you can take complete, accurate notes later, and bring two recorders in case one fails.
- *Phone interviews* are for interviewing those who are geographically distant or too busy to meet with you.
- *E-mail interviews*, although not as personal, are convenient for most people. E-mail exchanges allow asking follow-up questions to the interviewee's responses and provide digital files for later reference; however, they take longer and typically do not elicit as much information.
- *Messaging interviews* are conducted over the Internet using messaging software. They allow you to type at or talk to people far away in real time. You can adapt your questions to their responses, as in a phone interview. Typed text messages are slower; some people do not type answers quickly and will not give lengthy answers. However, web cam and voice communication, available now on messaging services, allow you virtual face-to-face interviewing.

Be courteous and professional in an interview. Explain who you are and why you want to talk with the person. Don't be discouraged, though, if someone is unwilling to be interviewed.

- Prepare by learning about the person you will be interviewing so that your questions will meet that person's needs as well as yours. By so doing, you will find the interviewee more open and cooperative in providing you with needed information.
- Begin an interview with small talk to make your interviewee comfortable.
- Avoid biased questions that assume what they ask or that encourage your interviewee to respond in a specific manner, two-in-one questions, confusing or wordy questions, and questions unrelated to your subject of investigation.
- Listen to responses and follow them up with questions to elicit more information.
- Respect the person you are interviewing; never push questions in an area that makes the interviewee uncomfortable.
- Keep the person you are interviewing on topic. If the conversation drifts, redirect it to the subject at hand.

Report your information accurately; do not take interview responses out of context or otherwise misrepresent the interviewee's responses.

## ASSESSING YOUR PRIMARY RESEARCH

Assess your primary research data before writing it up.

- Consider all factors potentially related to your data, even if they were not studied or quantified.
- Review your methodology. Biased methods yield biased results.
- Collect enough detail that someone could repeat the experiments to verify the results.
- Be specific; include all measurements and relevant observations.
- Consider that if two results show a relationship in your data, one does not necessarily cause the other.

- Draw general conclusions carefully from the data. Identify patterns or trends, but do not assume that what you have found is characteristic of all times and places.
- Know which data are valid. Some experimental results should be omitted because of circumstance, such as equipment malfunction. Distinguish systematic from random errors in the data; distinguish precision, the degree to which further measurements show the same values, from accuracy, the degree to which a measured quantity agrees with its value.
- Understand the role and value of statistical tools for specifying confidence in experimental results.

# SECONDARY RESEARCH

## THE VALUE OF SECONDARY RESEARCH

You will need to use other people's information and ideas to supplement your own information and to validate your inferences and recommendations in your own reporting. Scientific work requires that you compare your results with those of others who have done similar work and published it in the technical literature.

Secondary sources provide you with technical information, concepts, and techniques that help you to solve on-the-job problems and complete your own work successfully.

Nonetheless, you cannot simply copy what others have written into your own documents. Instead, you will need to absorb, evaluate, and summarize their work within your own. You will also need to cite these secondary sources every time you use them.

Organize and express the material from secondary sources to support your own writing goals. Write them clearly, so that you and your reader can learn and benefit from this kind of research.

## FINDING INFORMATION

We live in an information age. The amount of information publicly available is unprecedented in human history and continues to increase at a geometric rate. As you begin to look for sources of information, you must develop good habits for finding, evaluating, and selecting the information that you need to complete your writing project.

---

FACTORS AFFECTING CHOICE OF INFORMATION SOURCES

**For the Student**
Identifying a topic for a student paper can be frustrating or bewildering. You can feel caught between two realities: your own interests and the limitations of the situation. Consider these questions.

- What are your own interests in this subject area?
- How much scope has the professor given you to choose your topic?
- How much do you know already about this subject?
- What are your deeper concerns and values in this subject area?
- What are the practical limitations of your research?
- What sources of authoritative information are available to you at your college or university?
- How much time do you have for research, allowing time for writing after research?

Research is a process of balancing inner needs with outer realities: your needs to learn and to produce a high-quality paper with a good final grade versus finding pertinent, available sources of information within the allotted time.

**For the Working Professional**

Most working documents come from working situations where the audience and purpose are already known. You do not have to search for a suitable topic—it is given to you. The boss may say, "Write up what you've been doing to improve our monitoring facility, and have the report on my desk by next Friday noon."

The main content of your report will be primary sources, your own data collected as you worked. Often, you will need to consult secondary sources to confirm your findings and to provide useful inferences to analyze your data. Such sources can be found in libraries, online, and in company or government files. Networking with other technical professionals is an important way to compare notes, find solutions to technical problems, and track sources of information.

Working situations have deadlines. The time available for research will determine the number and choice of information sources for your project.

# INSTITUTIONAL SOURCES OF INFORMATION

Information can be found in institutions, such as libraries or government archives, and in various forms, including books, periodicals, and multimedia.

## LIBRARIES

Libraries are stocked with reliable, current sources of information organized in a consistent way to make them accessible. Most public libraries in North America use the Library of Congress system for organizing their holdings. You will find library staff helpful and well informed. The library is the ideal place to begin your research.

### COLLEGE LIBRARIES

College and university libraries typically hold resources that cover the fields of knowledge taught in their particular programs or departments. Although serving their particular faculty and students, these libraries welcome the working public who have practical uses for their information. Consult the librarians for conditions of access.

College libraries typically provide access to both print and electronic media, and most network with other college libraries across North America to provide even wider access. This arrangement gives college students access to a remarkable range of potential sources of information.

### PUBLIC LIBRARIES

Public libraries in local municipalities also hold resources in broad fields of knowledge: generally, the larger the municipality, the larger the library holdings. Public archives, for example, may have detailed architectural drawings of important buildings under renovation or plans of municipal infrastructure of use to an engineer.

Note that many older libraries in smaller municipalities still use the Dewey Decimal system of organizing their information. Consult the local librarian.

### COMPANY LIBRARIES

Large companies and government departments have libraries that hold resources in areas of particular interest to their staffs. Many companies now contract with private or government databases for electronic information that relates to company projects.

Get to know your local staff. They are the gatekeepers of the information in the library. They are also professional people who can help you find the information you need for your project.

With so many potential sources of information to choose from, you will save time and frustration by learning new library research skills each time you visit and by asking questions of the helpful, trained staff. For example, a librarian can show you indexes of periodical literature, published books, government documents, maps and charts, or industrial guides.

## COMPANIES AND AGENCIES

Many companies and government agencies have extensive reports in their files on company or agency activities. These can provide information on previous work done on projects like yours, technical specifications and data that reduce the amount of investigation you need for your project, and samples of the style and format typical of reports and other documents submitted in your company.

Note that some information in company files is confidential or sensitive in nature. It is important to ask permission to use such information and to observe company policy and best practice.

Companies and governments now also maintain extensive internal computer networks with databases of information accessible only by employees with logins and passwords. This information has the advantage of being relevant and up-to-date. Company intranets can link employees distributed across wide geographical areas in real time to exchange ideas and information in a variety of digital forms, including text, images, and video.

## THE INTERNET

The World Wide Web is enormous and is still growing at an unprecedented rate. The Internet Systems Consortium has charted more than 500 million hosts; the number of actual systems on the Internet is in the billions and growing. The best search engines can catalogue only a fraction of the information stored on the Web.

In this situation, finding specific information on the Internet can be frustrating. Information turned up in web searches can be shallow, misleading, or wrong. It often takes valuable time to search out specific, useful information because the most common uses of the Internet—shopping, financial transactions, games, and travel—do not include technical applications for the workplace.

For these reasons, it is important to learn the most efficient ways of searching for what you need.

### WEBSITES: THE PUBLIC WEB

The volume of information—and misinformation—on the Web is immense, and not every keyword search leads to immediate or good results. Online searching using search engines and directories can be time consuming and frustrating. Online sources, especially websites, must therefore be evaluated carefully before their information is used.

You may want to ask yourself the following questions to guide your evaluation of a website. Develop a portfolio of useful websites in your web browser for quicker access to needed information in subject areas relevant to your field of study or work needs.

The most informative websites are regularly updated with new information, revisions of content, and restructuring to provide better access to information. Indicators that care has been taken to provide current, authoritative information include the following:

- good navigation links
- logical hierarchy of pages within the website
- clear and correct use of English
- balanced amounts of specific detail on each page
- identification of the person or agency responsible for website content
- authority of content established by the citing of sources or by the reputation of the company or agency providing the information

An example of a reputable company providing technical information on its website is Baroid Industrial Drilling Products: their website offers technical assistance for drillers, a research and development lab, and application data for its drilling products.

Websites maintained by individuals are more problematic and prone to bias and misinformation, but some can be informative and reliable, as long as you can identify a qualified and reliable source of information.

## WEBSITES: THE PRIVATE WEB

Controlling access to information in industry is important because of trade secrets and patents. Thus private companies and government agencies protect confidential or sensitive files of information on their intranets with password securities of various kinds available to employees. Intranets provide opportunities for employees in geographically diverse locations to exchange information as needed.

Clients and contractors can also be given access to such information as is necessary to work with company employees. This kind of "extranet" provides information about tools, applications, sales, project management, technical specifications and manuals, company policies, business standards, and training. It also provides opportunity for collaboration with company employees in the form of e-mail, chat rooms, and threaded discussion forums, in which all responses to an initial question are kept together in the same area of the forum in chronological order.

## GOVERNMENT SERVICES

Government websites provide information services to the working public, everything from how to apply for building permits to how current weather conditions will affect farmers. Their services include, but are not limited to archives, technical information, statistics, geographical databases, current regulations, and directories of government departments and functions.

# TYPES OF SOURCES

## ENCYCLOPEDIAS

Browsing an encyclopedia can help you learn more about a subject by providing an overview and suggesting interesting topic areas to explore further. Simplified diagrams, for example, can show structures in a plant, energy flow in a hydraulic system, or the cycle of a four-stroke engine.

However, an encyclopedia does not provide the detail required in a professional document. It is background reading to give direction to your research, not the final source of information. Students should avoid citing encyclopedia articles as sources in college papers; the articles are too broad in scope and sometimes lack enough authority to be reliable.

Complete articles from professionally edited, online encyclopedias, such as Encyclopedia Britannica and Microsoft Encarta, require paid subscriptions. If your college library has paid subscriptions to such services, then you may use them as background reading to guide your search for information.

---

### WIKIPEDIA

Wikipedia is an open-source, online encyclopedia with significant attraction for students: it is convenient to use, informative on selected topics, and hyperlinked to related articles. It attempts to harness the collaborative power of the Internet to collect and synthesize human knowledge, but there are problems.

Wikipedia has shortcomings that may not be obvious to students, and in response to these, some North American university departments have banned the use of Wikipedia entirely. Here are the arguments:

- Wikipedia has no contributing editors; its contributors are unregulated and anonymous.
- While Wikipedia asks its contributors to identify their sources of information and to write in clear, unbiased language, many choose not to do so. As a result, many entries lack detail or cited authority for assertions, or express ideas poorly.

---

WIKIPEDIA, *continued*

- Recent articles are generally less complete and more biased than established ones.
- Controversial subjects have given rise to "edit wars." Wikipedia has had to list "protected pages" that cannot be edited because of vandalism and differing points of view on an issue.
- Wikipedia articles include warnings of incompleteness, the use of "weasel words," lack of citations, and so on.

Wikipedia is an ongoing work that may have significant value in the future. Current new projects like Wiktionary, a comprehensive dictionary of languages, and Wikispecies, a complete taxonomy of living species for scientific users, may develop into databases of potential benefit to many users.

Much of Wikipedia, however, is still problematic. Use at your own risk. Read critically. While Wikipedia has some value in leading students to citable sources, it is not an appropriate source for citation. Students should read the Wikipedia section called "Researching with Wikipedia" before using the site.

# BOOKS

Published books are written, reviewed, and edited to ensure a standard of language and information. While not perfect, the process provides the reader with a measure of reliability.

Currency is important in science and technology. Texts published more recently will generally refer to a broader base of knowledge and more current technologies. Some texts give a broad overview of a subject; some are specialized and illustrated in detail; some are casebooks containing a series of articles on the same subject by a variety of experts with varying points of view. Each has its own audience and purpose. Read the introduction and contents pages to gain a sense of those and how useful they would be for your own paper.

E-books and electronic databases are replacing print manuals and catalogues because they are cheaper and easier to keep current with technological change. Naturally, the computer industry has led the way in this area, but e-books are now available in science, engineering, ecology, construction trades, auto mechanics, and many other technical subject areas.

# PERIODICALS

Periodicals are magazines and journals published for specific groups of working professionals. Their purpose is to keep their specialized audiences informed of the latest scientific and technical developments in the field, so their information is the most up-to-date available publicly.

Of particular interest to the researcher are peer-reviewed journals, ones with articles that have been read and approved by a panel of experts. Review assures the accuracy of the information in an article to a significant degree.

Get to know the most useful and respected journals in your field of study. As you become more experienced, you will find these an increasingly useful resource. Libraries have current and bound back issues of journals in many fields. Many have back issues of periodicals available on CD-ROM.

Many professional journals now publish online. For a subscription fee, you can have current issues sent to your inbox or browse back issues on the publisher's website. Many libraries subscribe to online searchable databases of journal articles, such as Ebscohost and Proquest. These give you access to a wide range of articles in specific subject areas.

## MULTIMEDIA

Information for training and sales in industry is disseminated today in multimedia forms. Technical communication requires both language and graphic forms to deliver a complete message. Digital forms of communication—photography, digital video, presentation software, audio files, and so on—are now common and important ways to publish and distribute technical information.

College, public, government, and company libraries have audio-visual areas with catalogued resources on videotape, CD-ROM, and DVD, as well as online access to digital media by agreement with companies or government agencies.

Many new forms of digital storage and transmission are appearing. These allow more information to be distributed in more different forms using more compact media. This wide availability makes it more important than ever for a researcher to allocate enough time to consider all options and to choose information sources wisely and selectively.

## GOVERNMENT PUBLICATIONS

The federal and provincial governments of Canada publish thousands of pamphlets, brochures, and booklets every year with useful scientific and technical information. These are usually catalogued and shelved separately from other publications; consult your local librarian. Many are now available on government websites.

Government sources are particularly useful when your project has to take into account laws and the regulations passed under those laws. Governments set standards for everything from road safety to water quality. These technical parameters are often set out as brochures and reports of various kinds.

## ONLINE DATABASES

Governments and private companies make information gathered through government agencies, such as Natural Resources Canada, Agriculture Canada, the Geological Survey of Canada, or Statistics Canada, publicly available to technical professionals. Examples of current Internet databases include the following:

- GeoGratis: This series of online databases maintained by Natural Resources Canada contains geographic information about the Canadian land base in vector, raster, and tabular formats; it is useful for engineers, land-use planners, foresters, GIS technologists, and so on.
- Statistics Canada: Information about Canada and Canadians is useful for business professionals who market products and services provided by engineering and technical companies.
- Dialog: In the private sector, Dialog is one of the oldest online companies to provide access by subscription to databases in many fields of knowledge.

## NETWORKING

Networking is an informal, but important dimension of the research process for a working professional. A network of colleagues begins to develop at college and continues throughout one's career, supported by correspondence, telephone conversations, and meetings at conferences and other professional gatherings.

Your network can be broadened on the Internet with names and e-mail addresses of professionals working in your field. Colleagues in your network can direct you to good sources of information for your report or even provide you directly with information and insights. Some informal types of reports allow the use of information from an informal network. Some documentation systems require citing personal, unpublished sources of information; consult your documentation system for further guidance.

The Internet connects working professionals with one another and with useful technical information. Networking via e-mail can be useful in finding custom solutions to technical problems. Questionnaires sent to likely sources of information can achieve results if you are selective and know how to construct an online survey. Keep in mind that most e-mail questionnaires are spam, so it is important to word your subject line and introductory paragraph clearly to establish your authenticity.

# COMPLETING YOUR RESEARCH

## MAKING NOTES

Read through the information that you have collected and select what is most relevant to your audience and purpose; then, make notes on all the important points. Write down brief topic headings, using the key words found in the text.

This process puts the research into your head and lets your unconscious mind begin to work on it, so that when you begin to draft, the information you need for the text of your document will be there. More important, connections will become clear. The data will begin to be understandable.

Writing is a process of discovery. It lets us make sense of our world.

## INTERPRETING YOUR RESEARCH

The technical writer's work is not just gathering and summarizing facts, though that is the primary goal. The reader will want to know what the facts mean, what they signify. The writer is responsible for providing interpretation, analysis, or inferences.

At any point in the writing process, you will find ideas popping into your head. These will help you to see the big picture, to figure out what your information means. Ideas or insights can come from your own training and experience or be found in your research materials.

New ideas are important, for example, when your purpose in writing is to understand a situation better or solve a problem. Like a doctor who listens to the patient's problem, selects tests, and observes the results, you can formulate a diagnosis as you use the writing process to work through the details. You might also find out how to solve the problem.

Write these ideas down as you do the research. At the end of the research, review them. They will form the basis for your conclusions. You can add to them later as you organize, draft, and revise your document.

## INFERENCES

Inferences are conclusions drawn about what we don't know based on what we do know. The automotive technician hears a distinctive noise coming from the car's engine and infers that the motor has a loose tappet. Inferences can be drawn from data in different ways. Generally, the more training and experience one has, the more accurate the inferences one can draw from data.

Inferences are an important part of your report. The analysis after the presentation of information tells the reader what the data mean and what next steps are appropriate. Research in secondary sources lets you review the facts and the inferences of others so that your own inferences can be as accurate and meaningful as possible.

Use your judgment about whether to explain in detail how you reached your inferences. Your audience will be your guide. Some readers will need to see how you have interpreted the facts. Some will find your conclusions self-evident and need no explanation.

Your field or lab notes will help you to see connections and interpret the results of your research. Your secondary sources will also help with ideas that connect the significant facts.

## CHECKLIST FOR RESEARCHING YOUR INFORMATION

Before you begin to organize your research, have you

- developed a research strategy?
- developed solid, detailed content?
- brainstormed the subject to identify areas needing research?
- prioritized your research needs?
- identified potential sources of information?
- allocated adequate time for research?
- collected all primary sources, such as field notebooks and lab and field data sheets?
- assessed your primary data?
- completed your secondary research?
- explored all possible sources in libraries and online?
- made notes on your secondary research?
- developed some analysis of the data?

# 3

# ORGANIZING YOUR RESEARCH

Organizing your research is the most important step in making your document accessible to your intended audience. Technical communication is full of detailed, specific information that will confuse the reader unless it is set out in clearly stated, logically ordered categories.

Problems often arise at this step. It's not that some writers organize their research poorly. It's that they fail to organize at all. The consequences are severe:

- Attempting to draft a document straight from research notes without a plan leads to false starts and wasted effort; there is much more rewriting than necessary. The consequent confusion for the writer is stressful.
- Drafting and revising will go slowly, something that may result in missed deadlines at school or in the workplace.
- The same information will turn up in different places in the manuscript. The reader expects the writer to introduce a topic, explain it, and conclude it to move on to the next topic.
- Much research goes unused—a wasted effort.
- Communication is lost. Career opportunities become curtailed because writing is part of the job.

Plan a deadline to end your research. Leave enough time to organize materials before you draft, revise, and edit your paper.

Leaving adequate time to organize has many benefits, including time for reflection on your subject and time for further research if reading the assembled notes shows a need for more information. Your writing process will be shorter and more efficient if you complete the research before organizing the information and drafting the paper. Adding critical content during the later stages of a draft document creates work in reorganizing and rewriting parts of the paper.

Sometimes, such changes cannot be helped. The workplace will demand changes in response to new circumstances. A sound initial organization plan will be easier to modify to meet such demands.

Having a clear idea of your audience's needs and your purpose for writing will help bring the research to a conclusion because you will know when you have all the information needed for the project.

## READING YOUR RESEARCH

Take time to read through the research you have gathered.

- Identify the main points required in your text. Language is most useful in organizing thoughts.
- Look for key words and phrases that are repeated in your notes. These express important ideas that include a significant amount of data to be communicated. Highlight these words and phrases with a text marker.
- Check for headings in your secondary research materials. They can provide good clues to the larger organizing principles. Your goal will be to identify the main areas of concern. The number of main headings you select depends on the total length of the document and the conventional format required.
- Sort your notes into groups according to the main topics you have identified. Use coloured markers or symbols to identify topic areas, or physically sort the notes into separate piles. Sorting also makes specific information easy to find in the drafting and revising stages of the writing process.

Reading through your notes also has the benefit of putting many of the details into your head, details that will reappear when you draft.

## THE VALUE OF HEADINGS

Technical information is detailed and complex. That is why writing about technology requires careful and rigorous organization of specific topic areas under descriptive headings.

Compare a scientific article or technical report with a college essay. The essay begins with a topic or thesis statement, a sentence or two that captures the main subject in a few key words. It then explores that theme in a loosely connected series of paragraphs that move from one aspect of the subject to another.

Technical information cannot be communicated effectively in this way. Good technical communication begins with a statement of purpose and an outline of main topics that are identified throughout the document by a series of major and minor headings.

Headings benefit the reader in three ways.

- They create a simple context for complex details, a set of related, general ideas expressed as headings. With structure comes understanding. Organized detail becomes knowledge. Headings provide readers with a mental map to follow as they read through your document.
- Headings provide access. Technical readers often seek specific information in a document, not a connected argument, and embedded headings help to locate information efficiently. Few readers of technical literature read sequentially from beginning to end of text. They are searchers, looking for headings to access precisely the information they need and nothing more.
- Headings provide a standardized and consistent set of terms to assist readers in locating the detail they need in your text.

To provide these benefits, you must create an outline, an organizational scheme to make the structure of your data clear to your reader and provide access to it. A good outline arises partly from the information itself and partly from the mind of the writer who imposes order on the detail.

Outlining benefits the writer in three ways.

- Outlining keeps similar information together and reveals its structure and meaning. It provides an important aid to the writer because you cannot communicate what you do not understand. Organizing your information lets you understand it better; consequently, your written text will become more meaningful and accessible for your reader.
- Outlining saves time. The time you will need to rewrite a disorganized draft is far greater than the time it takes to outline: to identify your main points, put them in a logical sequence, and write descriptive headings for them.
- Outlining also saves stress. Having a clear plan of work saves the worry of what to say next in your draft. Drafts that are completed quickly and read clearly give a sense of accomplishment.

# ■ THE OUTLINING PROCESS

Outlining is the process of creating a descriptive heading for each significant topic covered in a technical document. The technical writer outlines by reading through all researched materials, identifying significant topic areas, and writing descriptive headings for each one.

## THE GOAL OF THE OUTLINE

An outline is a logical structure of ideas, expressed as headings, that makes clear relationships within and among the data described by those headings. It is an information hierarchy similar to the structure of a database.

The goal of writing an outline is to create a classification system with mutually exclusive classes. No information in the document should appear in two or more sections.

Choose words for your headings that describe the content precisely. The thesaurus has synonyms to help you choose the words that best describe your data. Keep your audience in mind; some audiences need simpler, nontechnical vocabulary.

## READING YOUR NOTES

Complete your research and read over your notes. The goal is to gain an overview of the whole data set so that its structure becomes clearer to you. Only then can you begin to articulate that structure, to put words to it in the form of headings that make up the outline.

If you have electronic files or photocopies, make handwritten summaries. Writing by hand is a physical process that helps most writers to fix detail in their minds.

## FINDING THE MAIN TOPICS

From your notes, identify the main topic areas, subjects that cover a significant amount of detail and represent major theme. Do not be distracted by small-but-interesting facts.

The number of main topics will depend on the planned length of your document. More data means more significant areas of discussion. For a document of 1500 to 2000 words, three or four main areas, each representing approximately 20 to 30 percent of the material, are sufficient. Technical writers sometimes make the mistake of creating too many main topic headings. Used to working with detail, they see a long series of small issues in a set of research notes, instead of taking a broader view and seeing the larger issues that contain the smaller issues.

Express each main subject as a topic heading. A topic heading consists of a noun and its modifiers: "Refraction *of Light Using Gamma-ray Bursts.*" Use key words from your research notes, the words and phrases that express the really important ideas and that recur in notes from different sources. Use a marker pen to highlight significant terms in your research notes. Use the highlighted text to guide the choice of words for your main headings.

Your headings should describe specific content. Vague or abstract headings, such as "Miscellaneous" or "General Information," do not help your reader to identify information of interest. Question headings—"Should Gamma-rays Be Preferred to Optical Prisms in Light Studies?"—are informal; they are better suited to popular science writing.

Arrange your headings in a logical sequence that uses a basic organizing principle, such as time, space, cause-and-effect, typology, or more-to-less important.

---

**EXAMPLE OF OUTLINE—MAIN HEADINGS**

**Optical Processes in Compound Semiconductors**
**I. Absorption Processes**
**II. Light Emission Processes**
**III. Refraction and Diffraction Processes**

---

## GROUPING TOPICS INTO SUBHEADINGS

Read through your notes that cover the first main topic area. What are the main points within that first pile of notes? Identify the key words and phrases. Create subheadings for those subjects, using those same key words and phrases.

Continue to work through each main heading, selecting subtopics and writing key-word headings.

---

**OUTLINE WITH SUBHEADINGS**

**Optical Processes in Compound Semiconductors**
**I. Absorption Processes**
   **A. Band to Band**
   **B. Quantum Well**
   **C. Impurity Level**
   **D. Free Carrier**
**II. Light Emission Processes**
   **A. Emission Process Types**
   **B. Transitions by Radiation**
   **C. Recombination Processes**
**III. Refraction and Diffraction Processes**
   **A. Directing Light**
   **B. Guiding Light**

---

## GROUPING TOPICS INTO THIRD LEVELS AND BEYOND

Continue this process with the subheadings, breaking them into smaller units of information, until each of the smallest topic areas can be written from your notes into about two or three paragraphs. Technical documents of 20 or more pages will typically display at least three levels of organization.

Ensure that headings at each level of organization contain at least two subheadings, except for the lowest level of headings. Doing this creates balance in your outline and in your document. Also ensure that the sequence of headings at each level of organization is logical. Often, a consistent plan of organization, such as more-to-less important, classification, or cause-and-effect, will exhibit itself and can be repeated under a series of headings at the same level of organization.

---

OUTLINE WITH THREE LEVELS OF ORGANIZATION

Optical Processes in Compound Semiconductors
I.  Absorption Processes
    A. Band to Band
        1. Direct Gap
        2. Indirect Gap
        3. Excitons
    B. Quantum Well
        1. Interband
        2. Intraband
    C. Impurity Level
    D. Free Carrier
II. Light Emission Processes
    A. Emission Process Types
        1. Spontaneous
        2. Stimulated
    B. Transitions by Radiation
        1. Radiative
        2. Nonradiative
    C. Recombination Processes
        1. Band to band
        2. Mid-gap levels
        3. Auger
        4. Stimulated
III. Refraction and Diffraction Processes
    A. Directing Light
    B. Guiding Light

---

Notice in the example that the number of headings under each main heading is not exactly equal. The principles of outlining do not require that each main section of a document contain exactly equal numbers of subheadings or of written content measured in words, but the sections should be approximately equal for balance.

## FORMATTING YOUR OUTLINE

A formal outline has a conventional structure that allows a writer to see the structure of the writing plan clearly and follow its logic and balance from draft to revision to the final document.

- The working title of the document sits at the top of the outline, centred.
- Main headings are numbered with Roman numerals and sit on the left margin.
- Secondary headings are indented five spaces and numbered with upper case letters. Third-level headings are indented 10 spaces and numbered with Arabic numerals.
- Heading conventions for outlines can accommodate 10 levels of organization or more. The more content in a document, the more levels of organization are required.

## CHECKING YOUR OUTLINE

Use the following checklist of outline characteristics to ensure proper balance and coordination of elements in the organization of your headings:

- heading words: key words and phrases describe the content of the heading section clearly and concisely.
- parallelism: similar content in different sections of the document requires similar phrasing of headings.
- subordination: content under any heading relates to that heading.
- coordination: similar content in different sections of the document requires similar organization plans at the secondary levels.
- logical order: sequencing of major and minor elements in the outline reflects a logical progression of ideas, such as problems-solutions, more-to-less important, or cause and effect.
- balance: roughly equal amounts of information in the main sections of the document tell the reader that all areas of content are equally important.
- title: a working title expresses the main theme of the paper.

## ■ COMMON ORGANIZATION PLANS

Knowing and making appropriate use of common patterns of organization will help you in creating an outline. Commonly understood patterns of organizing thoughts will allow you to recognize patterns within your own research. The outline will also be more logical, and the final document based on the outline will make better sense to your reader.

Use the following patterns of organization to guide how you think about your research. They are not data sheets with rigid categories to be filled in. They are models to help you to recognize the shapes of information in your research, blueprints that make your thinking clearer to your reader. As you develop your outline, patterns can be changed, modified, or combined as needed to fit the information you are organizing.

## MORE-TO-LESS IMPORTANT ORDER

Executive readers want to know what you consider to be the most important factors. The order that you choose for the presentation of your information indicates your evaluation of the data. Put your strongest reasons first. Check your headings to ensure that they describe your data completely and accurately.

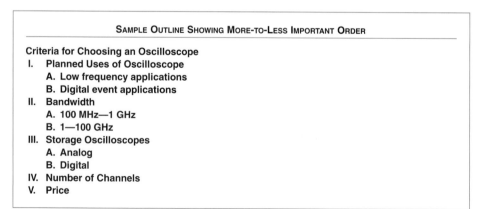

SAMPLE OUTLINE SHOWING MORE-TO-LESS IMPORTANT ORDER

Criteria for Choosing an Oscilloscope
I.   Planned Uses of Oscilloscope
     A. Low frequency applications
     B. Digital event applications
II.  Bandwidth
     A. 100 MHz—1 GHz
     B. 1—100 GHz
III. Storage Oscilloscopes
     A. Analog
     B. Digital
IV.  Number of Channels
V.   Price

# PROBLEM-SOLUTION ORDER

This pattern follows the logical sequence of investigating a workplace problem and proposing a solution.

1. Define the problem. Much time can be wasted investigating a problem that has not been clearly defined. Identify what is not working and describe it. Alternately, identify an opportunity to improve current systems. It may be necessary to review the history of long-standing problems and attempted solutions.
2. Investigate the problem thoroughly and methodically. Begin by confirming the problem's technical parameters so that time is not wasted trying to fix a problem that doesn't exist. Use standard methods of investigation. Set out the reasons for choosing a particular methodology, the steps in the procedure, and the technologies employed.
3. Present solutions in a "Recommendations" section. Avoid a natural tendency to overstate the solutions and to draw attention to your role in determining them.

When using this plan for your document, remember that most investigators report to supervisors who want to know the solution first. It is therefore wise to begin the document with an executive summary.

---

### SAMPLE OUTLINE SHOWING PROBLEM-SOLUTION ORDER

**Managing The Municipal Waste Stream**
I.   The Municipal Waste Problem
   A. Volume of Waste
      1. Accelerating rates, 1980–2007
      2. Projected increase to 2030
   B. Composition of the Waste Stream
      1. Food
      2. Paper
      3. Metals and polymers
II.  Municipal Waste Management Options
   A. Resource Recovery
      1. Processes and products
      2. Advantages and disadvantages
   B. Recycling
      1. Processes and products
      2. Advantages and disadvantages
   C. Incineration
      1. Processes and products
      2. Advantages and disadvantages
   D. Landfill
      1. Processes and products
      2. Advantages and disadvantages

---

The problem-solution pattern can also be used in persuasive writing, as in the following example where safety is a central concern.

**Safe Operation Of Drilling Equipment**
I.  Cost of Unsafe Operation
    A. Equipment Repair and Replacement
    B. Personal Injury
II. Responsibilities of Owners and Operators
    A. Proactive Approach
    B. Correcting Hazards
    C. Equipment
        1. Intended uses of equipment
        2. Limits and tolerances of equipment
    D. Compliance with Regulations
    E. Supervisors and Employees
III. Maintenance of Equipment
    A. Manufacturer's Guidelines
    B. Observing Working Conditions
    C. Warning Labels
IV. Daily Inspections
    A. Personal Protective Gear
    B. Employee Training
    C. MSDS Sheets

## COMPARISON ORDER

Comparison is a pattern widely used in technical writing for evaluating methods and results. First, establish criteria by which the evaluation will take place: the needs and standards by which the data will be judged. Prioritize your criteria to distinguish more from less important factors.

You can make whole-by-whole or part-by-part comparisons. In whole-by-whole, each item or process is assessed in turn according to each of the set criteria. This structure works better for brief comparisons. In part-by-part, each criterion is applied in turn to each of the items or processes being compared. This structure works better for longer, more detailed comparisons.

**Oscilloscope Comparison**
I.  Criteria for Assessing Oscilloscopes for Company Purchase
    A. Bandwidth
    B. Sampling Rate
    C. Number of Channels
    D. Price
II. Tektronix Oscilloscopes
    A. Bandwidth
    B. Sampling Rate
    C. Number of Channels
    D. Price
III. LeCroy Oscilloscopes
    A. Bandwidth
    B. Sampling Rate
    C. Number of Channels
    D. Price
IV. Recommendations

## CLASSIFICATION ORDER

Classification is putting items with the same characteristics into the same category. Categories can contain subcategories. This process is used for creating an outline from a set of raw data.

The complementary process is partition. It begins with a broad topic area and partitions it into increasingly finer categories. Technical descriptions of instruments, mechanisms, or processes use this plan.

Use the method that best suits your audience and purpose. Focus on one characteristic at a time when creating categories to avoid overlap. Classifications should include all significant data sets in the research. Arrange classifications in a logical order such as by time or geographical area. The following section shows several common types of logical order.

---

**SAMPLE OUTLINE SHOWING CLASSIFICATION ORDER**

**Engineering Classification Of Soils**
I. Sands and Gravels
   A. Loose
   B. Dense
   C. Slightly Cemented
II. Silts
   A. Soft or Loose
   B. Firm or Dense
III. Clays
   A. Very Soft
   B. Soft
   C. Firm
   D. Stiff
   E. Very stiff
IV. Organic Soils and Peats
   A. Firm
   B. Spongy
   C. Plastic

---

## CHRONOLOGICAL ORDER

A time sequence can be a simple-but-effective pattern to use with information that describes any sequence of events in real time. Examples would be electrical or electronic events or any historical sequence of events under examination.

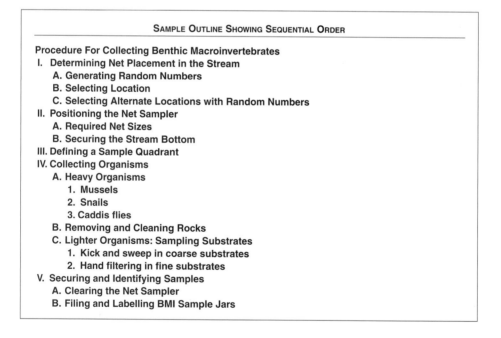

**Geological History Of Mount St. Helens**
I.  **Earliest Eruptions**
    A. Ape Canyon Stage—40,000 BP
    B. Cougar Stage—20,000 BP
    C. Swift Creek Stage—13,000 BP
II. **Spirit Lake Stage**
    A. Smith Creek Period—4500 BP
    B. Pine Creek Period—3200 BP
    C. Castle Creek Period—2400 BP
    D. Sugar Bowl Period—1400 BP
III. **Historic Era**
    A. Kalama Period—1480 AD
    B. Goat Rocks Period—1800 AD
IV. **Modern Era**
    A. Eruptions 1980 AD
    B. Ongoing Activity 1980—2007 AD

## SEQUENTIAL ORDER

Similar to chronological order, the sequential order pattern describes any procedure, usually performed by a technician or researcher.

**Procedure For Collecting Benthic Macroinvertebrates**
I.  **Determining Net Placement in the Stream**
    A. Generating Random Numbers
    B. Selecting Location
    C. Selecting Alternate Locations with Random Numbers
II. **Positioning the Net Sampler**
    A. Required Net Sizes
    B. Securing the Stream Bottom
III. **Defining a Sample Quadrant**
IV. **Collecting Organisms**
    A. Heavy Organisms
        1. Mussels
        2. Snails
        3. Caddis flies
    B. Removing and Cleaning Rocks
    C. Lighter Organisms: Sampling Substrates
        1. Kick and sweep in coarse substrates
        2. Hand filtering in fine substrates
V.  **Securing and Identifying Samples**
    A. Clearing the Net Sampler
    B. Filing and Labelling BMI Sample Jars

## SPATIAL ORDER

The spatial pattern gives your reader a mental picture of how something looks in two- or three-dimensional space. Used primarily for documents that describe geographical features, it can also be used for descriptions of equipment or instrumentation. In each case, a logical order must be established for the sequence of topics. For example, when describing the controls and their functions on an instrument panel, use a left-to-right or top-to-bottom sequence to keep your reader oriented. The following example uses a north-south line to order its geographical survey of resources.

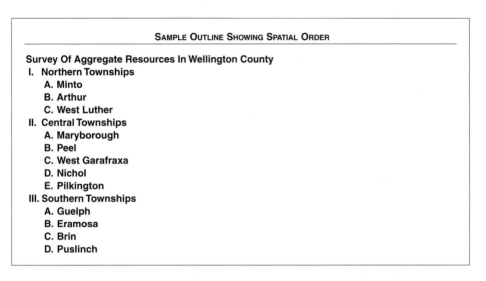

SAMPLE OUTLINE SHOWING SPATIAL ORDER

**Survey Of Aggregate Resources In Wellington County**
I.  **Northern Townships**
    A. Minto
    B. Arthur
    C. West Luther
II. **Central Townships**
    A. Maryborough
    B. Peel
    C. West Garafraxa
    D. Nichol
    E. Pilkington
III. **Southern Townships**
    A. Guelph
    B. Eramosa
    C. Brin
    D. Puslinch

# IMPLEMENTING THE OUTLINE

## WRITING HEADINGS INTO THE DRAFT

Use the headings from your outline to sort your notes and select research information to write up in the first draft.

Then, write the headings from your outline into your drafts together with the information from your notes. As you draft and revise, you may have to modify your outline because of circumstances or the need for change.

## HEADING CONVENTIONS

Use a simple graphic hierarchy to distinguish major from minor headings in your drafts. Adopt whatever is conventional in your company, college, or agency. Consider the following example.

FIRST-LEVEL HEADING
Second-level Heading
Third-level Heading

Further elaboration for a fourth and fifth level is possible in longer documents, which in a complex discussion may also use numbered headings to identify sections in sequence more clearly.

## CHECKLIST FOR ORGANIZING YOUR RESEARCH

Before you begin to draft, have you

- allowed the time needed to organize your research materials?
- read through your research materials, making notes and marking highlights?
- understood the value of outlining?
- followed the outlining process to create a structure of headings?
- reviewed your outline to ensure that it includes all the required research materials?
- created topic headings that capture all your proposed content accurately?
- created a hierarchy of information with at least three levels of organization?
- formatted your outline, using conventional numbering and indentation?
- applied the checklist of outline characteristics?
- used one of the common organizational plans for all or part of your outline?

# DRAFTING YOUR DOCUMENT

Drafting consists of working the data in your research notes into a coherent narrative, using the headings from your outline as a guide. Drafting should be an uninhibited process of creation. Push forward relentlessly, guided by your outline. Do not stop to revise, edit, or renew research. Just write.

Do your best to ensure that your research is complete before you begin to draft. However, as you revise later on, you may find that you require more research to punch up sections of your document. Revising will be much easier if your first draft is coherent.

A professional audience for technical communication expects content. A common fault is underestimating an audience's need for accurate, detailed information. Pack as much specific information as possible from your notes into your first draft.

Think of your first draft as a frame. As an analogy, a carpenter does not build one side of a piece of furniture, finish it, and then build another side. The whole rough frame is made before the finishing of the wood can begin.

As you draft your document, you may often find ideas and insights about the data coming unbidden into your mind. Record these for consideration later. Such generalizations or reflections, though not part of the reported data, may be included in your analysis of the data at the end of the presentation.

## HOW TO APPROACH DRAFTING

### WORK ENVIRONMENT

Work in an environment that encourages your concentration and creativity. Some people write early in the morning, others late at night. Some listen to music, while others prefer silence. Some like isolation, a cabin in the deep woods, or a table in a crowded coffee shop. Find what inspires you and lets you focus on the work of drafting.

Working environments can pose distractions. Turn off the television or the radio talk show. Switch your phone to the answering service. Do not eat another bag of fig cookies. Writing means sitting still and focusing the mind, a taxing process. Body and mind will rebel. Know when to give in and when to keep on task.

## STARTING THE DRAFT

Each writer has a method of starting the first draft. Most writers select the starting point based on their own needs and the needs of the form in which they are writing. Here are some examples of how writers begin.

- The writer tackles the most difficult sections of the document first; these sections are likely to be the longest and most complex parts of the writing.
- The writer starts with simple, short sections in order to work up to the harder parts.
- The writer chooses where to start based on his or her own enthusiasms: "Which section do I want to write first?" This idea is not frivolous. The work of writing is demanding and sometimes tedious. Winston Churchill claimed that writing is 10 percent inspiration and 90 percent perspiration. So, if you feel inspired to sit down at the computer and compose a specific section, do it.
- The writer begins with the materials that seem most familiar and comfortable to work with.
- The writer works through the sections in order as a way to keep the sequence of information clear for the final draft.

An example of the latter writer working within a set form is the scientific writer. Most scientific and technical reports have a "Results" section that reports the findings of scientific research or the results of investigations or testing in the field or in the lab. Drafting the "Results" section first allows the technical writer to put details of the accumulated data into a logical order. The act of processing the data into words and sentences will help make the data clearer and analysis easier when the "Discussion" section of the paper is written. The required content in the final sections drafted—the introduction and recommendations, if any—will also become clearer as the results and discussion are written up.

## DISCOVERING WHAT YOU HAVE TO SAY

The process of composition is a process of discovery. As you work through the details of your research, finding words to express the facts and ideas in your head, you begin to understand them at a deeper level. As you do this, you will discover connections in the data that were not obvious to you before. You may recognize some of these connections from your training and experience. Some may be new and unexpected, and then you will have to dig further, going back to the research process if time is available in order to track down what the data in the research means.

Writing is an adventure. It is fun, exasperating, unpredictable, and ultimately rewarding. It is a personal growth experience and a professional step in your career. A well-written, clearly presented, strongly argued report will speak well of your technical and communication abilities.

Write first for yourself. Leave the process of connecting your draft with an audience to the revising and editing stages.

## ◼ THE FIRST DRAFT

Shorter pieces should be drafted straight through in one session, like an essay exam. This practice produces coherence in thinking, a central theme that carries through to the goal.

Longer pieces can be drafted in a series of sessions, the order of sections depending on the nature of the work.

Deadlines and word limits do not matter at the drafting stage. What counts is getting the main ideas into the form of words and pictures. Later, revising and editing will enable you to meet deadlines and word limits, as well as connect with the audience's needs, but in the first draft, just write all you need to say.

Share your first draft. Technical accuracy is the first requirement of technical communication, so e-mail your draft to colleagues and friends, and pay careful attention to their comments. If you have friends who are also good editors—aware of language issues and the audience for whom you are writing—seek their advice. You have the benefit of not depending on writing for your livelihood, so make it fun. Put your writing on display and let the expectations of others shape and sharpen your craft.

## WRITING CONCLUSIONS

Readers want to understand why your information is important to them. The end of your draft—conclusions or discussion—must meet that need. In your introduction, state clearly the purpose of your investigation; in your conclusion, show how your work fulfills that purpose.

## THE RULES OF LANGUAGE

A fundamental condition of writing—and all the arts—is that you have to learn the rules before you can break them. Some teachers tell students not to worry about spelling, grammar, or organization because they fear that students will become discouraged. Some simply misunderstand why the rules exist at all.

The rules of language exist for sound reasons. They reflect the natural structures of human language. We say things in conventional ways so that others will understand. Rules of spelling, syntax (grammar), usage, and punctuation exist in any language so that readers can understand what is written. Are the rules artificial? Yes, in the sense that we can let any sound or character represent any idea or experience we wish. But they are still useful and meaningful artifices.

Language is dynamic. Under the collective impact of human experience and needs, conventions of language change daily, but gradually. From the core structure that remains, the writer can create a text that will have meaning to many people.

Let the words flow in the first draft. Sitting in front of your laptop and worrying about the next word will not help you. Ignore the rules for the moment, and just write down your thoughts and information. Follow the plan you made when you looked at the data.

Begin revising and editing in the second and third drafts. You will modify these drafts to follow the rules of language and make your meaning clearer, but the purpose of the first draft is for you to express yourself.

## █ PRACTISING WRITING

Writers learn to write by writing. It is a hands-on craft. Besides writing a journal of your professional activities, keep notes on all your work and maintain a flow of correspondence. Take your laptop into the field with you or to the coffee shop when you take a break to review the morning's results. As you sit down to compose a first draft, you hone your writing skills and raise your comfort level with the task.

Do not wait to be inspired. Write. The physical act will get your mind moving on the subject to be explored and expressed in words. If some of this flow of words is not clear or correct, it can be improved by editing or discarded. Too often, I have seen students sitting at a computer, staring at a blank screen, unwilling to risk a mistake by typing something, or typing a quick paragraph and immediately deleting it as not good enough. This condition is sometimes called "writer's block," but that term fails to capture the many reasons why some people take so long to produce a draft.

Put the critical self away and write. The first draft is liberating. It will show you what you have learned and imbue you with a sense of accomplishment. Getting it right for your audience can come later.

Take breaks. When the words stop coming or the words on the screen make no sense, quit for a time. Exercise. Stay well. Physical and mental health are as important for the writer as they are for any working professional.

## WRITING AS PROFESSIONAL WORK

Writing is a serious business, not a romantic undertaking. It must be taken seriously—though not solemnly! When you treat your writing as a job, as a necessary part of your working life, you will find the energy to complete the writing well. Set aside time to do the job. Working scientists and technical staff typically spend 20 percent of their work week in writing tasks. Use the time to focus on writing instead of hurrying through it and ignoring essential steps.

You may have the drive to see an engineering project through to a successful completion. Use the same drive to see your writing project through to the end. Doing so will pay dividends both personally and professionally. You may not be a professional writer, but writing is a significant part of your professional life, and you are being paid to do it. Focus on the journey.

Learn from others. As you review your secondary sources for ideas and information for your draft, note what makes a piece of good technical communication and how other technical writers achieve certain effects in their narratives. You will find that good technical communications have

- strong patterns of organization
- precise terminology for concepts and functions
- accuracy of data interpretation

Strive for these too.

## DRAFTING GRAPHICS INTO TECHNICAL COMMUNICATION

### THE PURPOSE OF GRAPHICS IN TECHNICAL COMMUNICATION

Any written or media presentation of technical information will make extensive use of graphics. Digital photos, engineering schematics, and scientific tables are examples of essential types of technical communication.

The purpose of writing in words is to provide a coherent narrative of events and ideas and to organize technical information logically. The purpose of graphic communication is to compress information into a compact, more intuitive form and to express ideas that cannot fully be expressed in words.

### INTEGRATING TEXT AND GRAPHICS

Words and pictures must work together. Two media properly integrated make the communication powerful. Not integrated, they will clash and undermine each other. Good writers seek a balance and do not ignore one at the expense of the other.

Make notations in your first draft at the places where your text needs to be explained or enhanced by graphic communication. Think always about what the reader needs to hear about your subject, what the reader needs to see, and where the reader needs to see it.

## ADDING GRAPHICS TO THE FIRST DRAFT

Exactly when you begin to include graphic communication is up to you and is affected by the circumstances under which you write. Most technical writers note the placement of possible graphic presentations in the first draft and then develop their graphics while revising and editing. Revisions to your content may add or eliminate the need for a graphic, so it is more efficient to wait until the text is fully revised before developing graphics.

Strategic placement of a graphic in relation to text is important. Use your word processor or presentation software to fit a graphic to the text that first refers to, describes, or explains the data it illustrates. Pay careful attention to how the audience will receive this flow of information.

Ask yourself: "Do I need to explain some things before introducing the graphic, perhaps the purpose of using this technique, the goals of the research undertaken, or the methods used to test and derive data? Or is it better to introduce the graphic that summarizes the data first and then provide a narrative explanation of key parameters and possibly an interpretation of the table, chart, or graph?"

Read over your draft to check the placement of your graphics so that they fit into the narrative at the right moment for the reader. Graphics that lack a direct connection with any of the narrative should be assigned to the report appendix.

## TABLES AND FIGURES

Graphic presentations in technical communication take the form of tables and figures. Readers of scientific and technical literature often read the tables and figures first because they want to see the data being presented. If the data look interesting, they will read the text, which provides context and interpretation. Graphic presentations therefore must be self-sufficient, carrying enough information so that the data sets are clear without further information from the text.

## SCIENTIFIC TABLES

Tables are a precise form of statistical display. If you have raw data from your own experimental work or from the published work of others, you can select them from your notes and work them into your first drafts.

As you draft, place comments in your text, indicating where you want tables to complement your written descriptions. A common method is placing the comments in square brackets, like this: [Insert table: Lake Erie sampling data, trophic status]. In subsequent drafts, you will create the required tables and insert them at these points in the text. Be sure to number your tables in sequence throughout the draft.

Insert a reference to the table in the text, like this: ". . . as shown in the Lake Erie sampling data (see Table 2)." In this case, Table 2 will appear immediately below the text reference or at the top of the next page. Keeping the table with the discussion of the data allows your reader to see the raw information in the context of your discussion that explains and interprets the results.

Each table must be identified by a table number—in sequence throughout the document—and a descriptive title. A few sentences of description may be included. If the data for the table are borrowed from another source, include an appropriate citation (see example below). Place the table number and title above the figure.

Here is an example of a scientific table.

**Table 1.** Sediment trap particulate $CaCO_3$ dissolution fluxes in the Pacific Ocean. The diference between the mean carbonate flux in the upper trap and the lower trap defines the dissolution flux. In all but one of the deepwater cases, the $CaCO_3$ flux collected in the midwater trap is higher than the carbonate flux collected in the deepwater trap. The dissolution rates are derived from the differences in $CaCO_3$ sediment trap fluxes between the upper and lower sediment traps divided by the depth range between the traps.

| LOCATION | TRAP DEPTH RANGE (m) | DISSOLUTION RATE ($\mu$mol kg$^{-1}$ year$^{-1}$) | REFERENCE |
|---|---|---|---|
| Shallow sediment traps | | | |
| Northwestern Pacific | 100–1000 | 0.12 | (46) |
| Equatorial Pacific | 105–320 | 0.67 | (47) |
| Northwestern Pacific | 500–1000 | 0.02 | (48) |
| Northeastern Pacific | 200–1000 | 0.10 | (49) |
| Deep sediment traps | | | |
| Northwestern Pacific | 2000–4000 | 0.003-0.006 | (48) |
| Equatorial Pacific | 2300–3600 | 0.005-0.014 | (50) |
| 2°59.8′N  135°1.0′E | 1592–3902 | 0.012 | (51) |
| 4°7.5′N  136°16.6′E | 1769–4574 | 0.013 | (51) |
| 0°0.2′N  175°09.7′E | 1357–4363 | 0.005 | (51) |
| 0°01′N  175° 02′E | 2200–4300 | — | (52) |
| 13°00′N  175°01′E | 1500–5100 | 0.006 | (52) |
| 00°04′N  139°45′W | 2284–3618 | 0.005-0.014 | (50) |
| 11°58′S  135°02′W | 1292–3594 | 0.003 | (52) |
| 50°0′N  145°0′W | 1000–3800 | 0.024 | (49) |

Feely et al., 2004
**Figure 4.1** Example of a scientific table

Notice the features of table format, top to bottom:

- table number (in sequence through document) and title (complete, descriptive)
- heavy line separating title block from vertical column headings
- vertical column headings with abbreviated units of measurement
- line separating vertical column headings from data

Do not rule lines between vertical and horizontal column headings. Add a light line below the table if the text continues below the table on your printed page. Footnotes are permitted where necessary to explain individual statistics.

Notice that mathematical precision requires that you display numeric values to the appropriate number of significant digits.

## FIGURES

### FIGURE PURPOSE AND PLACEMENT

A figure is any visual display of data other than a table. Figures can be graphs, charts, diagrams, cutaway or exploded views, drawings, digital photos, or maps. Any figure must convey data to the viewer accurately and honestly.

As you draft, place comments in your text to indicate where figures should be inserted. Enclose these notes about placement in square brackets like this: [Insert figure: Biogeoclimatic Ecosystem Classification System Map, British Columbia].

In subsequent drafts, you will insert the required figures at these points in the text. Number your figures in sequence throughout the draft.

## FIGURE INTEGRATION AND IDENTIFICATION

Insert a reference to each figure into the text, like this: ". . . as seen in the Coastal Douglas Fir region (see map, Figure 2)." In this case, Figure 2 will appear immediately below the first text reference to it or at the top of the next page. Keeping the figure with the relevant section of narrative allows your reader to visualize your information in context.

Each figure must be identified by a figure number—in sequence throughout the document—and a descriptive title. A few sentences of description may be included. If the figure is borrowed from another source, include an appropriate citation (see example below). Place the figure number and title below the figure.

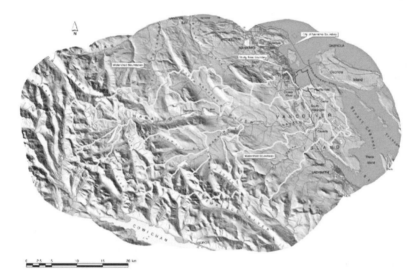

**Figure 1.** Map of the Nanaimo River watershed
*(Nanaimo Estuary Management Plan, 2008)*

**Figure 4.2**  Example of a figure

Note these common features of figure format:

- figure number (in sequence through document) and title (complete, descriptive), with citation if borrowed
- figure centred on page; small figures on right margin with text wrapped left
- no border, unless a map, which is customarily framed by a neat line
- blank line below title block to space it from figure

When creating your own figures, follow these conventions:

- Label parts of a figure directly on the figure wherever possible.
- Where direct labelling is not possible, use a legend (symbols) or a key (letters, numerals).

**Chapter 4** • Drafting Your Document

## TYPES OF FIGURES

Use a pie diagram to show parts of a whole data set.

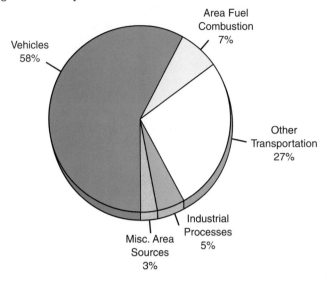

**Ontario Carbon Monoxide Emissions by Sector
(Emissions From Human Activity, 2001 Estimates)**

*(Ontario Ministry of the Environment, 2007)*

**Figure 4.3** Example of a pie diagram or graph

Use a bar chart to show tabular data. Ensure that the length of the bars varies with quantities represented.

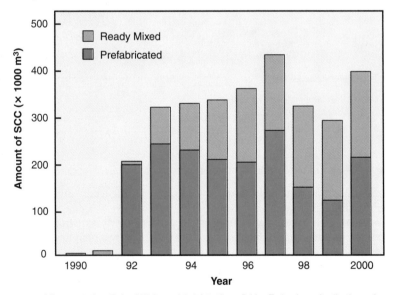

*(U.S. Department of Transportation, Federal Highway Administration—Bridge Technology: Applications of Self-Compacting Concrete in Japan, Europe and the United States)*

**Figure 4.4** Example of a bar graph

Use a graph to show trends or compare data sets.

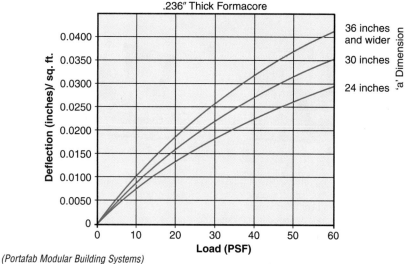

(Portafab Modular Building Systems)

**Figure 4.5** Example of a line graph

Use a block diagram to show processes or organizations of people.

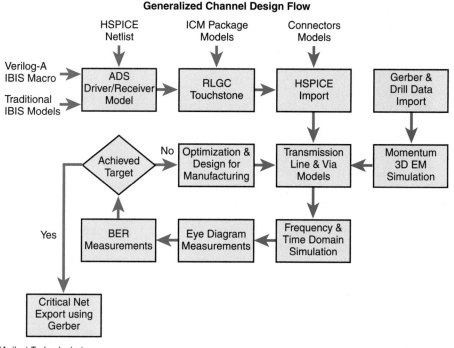

(Agilent Technologies)

**Figure 4.6** Example of a block diagram

Use a line drawing to clarify any process, idea, or structure.

**Comparison of Flex-Track and Rigid Frame
Crossing an Obstacle**

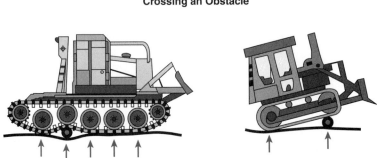

**Figure 30.** The weight on the rigid-frame suspension is concentrated at two points, but is spread out for the flex-track suspension. Furthermore, the rigid-frame suspension exerts a high-impact loading at the front of the track when it pivots over the obstacle.
*(British Columbia, Harvesting Systems and Equipment in British Columbia)*

**Figure 4.7** Example of line drawings

Use photographs to convey lots of information at a glance or to verify statements.

# ▌ DOCUMENTING YOUR SOURCES

If any part of your communication—text or graphics—includes materials borrowed from published sources, you must acknowledge those sources at the time and every time you use them. We document secondary sources for three reasons:

1. For ethics: Putting your name down as the author of a document means that you are claiming the work as original. If you have borrowed from others and not cited them, you have plagiarized.
2. For efficiency: Readers of technical communications want specific detail. Showing your sources gives readers the opportunity to get more detail on specific topics.
3. For authority: Especially in persuasive communications, cited authorities lend weight to an argument.

Document your secondary sources as you write the first draft. For the text passages you have paraphrased, insert appropriate citations of sources, using CSE or IEEE format. Later editing may change their sequence, but it is easier to work citations into your first draft than to comb a later draft for borrowed information.

Choose a standard documentation system, one appropriate to your workplace and professional discipline. Two major ones used in science, engineering, and technology are outlined in this text (see chapters 10 and 11). Learn the system thoroughly before applying it to your drafts.

Do not quote passages from secondary sources directly, unless the exact wording of the original is at issue. Put the text of your sources into your own words. Write a lead-in for each paraphrased section, referring to the author directly in the text, as in this example: "Kobayashi et al. (2006) found toroid eddy currents in the range of 150–250 mA for frequencies above 150 MHz."

## CHECKLIST FOR DRAFTING YOUR DOCUMENT

Before you begin to revise your drafts, have you

- completed your research?
- arranged your work environment to facilitate drafting?
- approached drafting in a way that suits you?
- created a first draft with all the main ideas formed into words and sentences?
- shared your first draft with colleagues and friends and asked for comments and suggestions?
- written a strong introduction and a logical conclusion?
- practised writing in various forms between drafting sessions?
- checked the first draft for the qualities of good technical communication?
- added notations where graphic presentations will be inserted?
- developed tables and figures to present your data and support your narrative?
- cited your secondary sources of information?

# REVISING AND EDITING

Revising and editing is the process of altering the first draft so that the document meets the needs of the intended audience and communicates more effectively.

Revising your work can be an adventure and a source of pride in work well done. The search for meaning is unpredictable. Insights are born suddenly. Alternatives present themselves. Words come unbidden to express what was previously only thought. Understanding grows, and insight adds richness to one's personal knowledge base.

## ■ MAKING REVISING AND EDITING A PRIORITY

Many technical professionals make revising and editing a low priority, giving it the least time of all the stages in the writing process. They write a draft and then "fix" it, taking a cursory glance that may catch minor problems. The submitted paper is likely hard to read and full of errors.

Procrastination is the most common reason for omitting this stage. Leaving a writing project to the last minute—leaving no time to revise and edit—results in a poor product that ultimately wastes time and damages reputations.

First drafts are never perfect and rarely connect with the intended audience. Disciplined revising and editing is necessary to achieve this connection. Every writer of technical and scientific literature must give this stage in the writing process adequate time and consideration. Samuel Johnson said that "what is written without effort is read without pleasure." In the revising and editing stage, you will make the effort to work out problems, correct errors, and succeed in connecting with your reader.

### MAKING MULTIPLE DRAFTS

When your first draft is completed, you have only begun to write. Author and management consultant Peter Drucker called his first draft the "zero" draft because that is when the real writing begins. Novelist Stephen King calls the first draft "the closed door" and the second "the open door" because the first draft is for the author alone and the second is for others to see.

Revising your first draft is the best way to connect with your reader. A writer's first draft is often disorganized and difficult to understand; however, even 20 minutes of opening it up, re-organizing it, adding important details, and rewriting descriptions can greatly improve your writing's power to communicate. Revising means facing your errors after you have had the satisfying experience of completing a draft. Have courage. Always take the time to revise.

Good writers are also their own most severe editors. Learn your language and apply its rules. Your reader can't get your message if the structures of your language are non-standard. Check your facts. A technical audience looks at them first.

## THE DISCIPLINE OF REVISING AND EDITING

Why won't someone else just understand what you've written in the first draft the way you do?

First, the experience of writing a first draft can be euphoric: "I did it!" But such feelings do not allow for sober second thought. Your draft may have many errors that will frustrate and confuse your reader. It's too easy to assume that the reader will know what you intended.

Second, specialists in technical fields use specialized language sets. Their vocabularies, short forms, and sentence structures are confusing to those who do not share their specialty. Many technical writers are not aware of the uniqueness of their specialized vocabularies and use technical terms—familiar to them—in a first draft. Doing so seems natural, but if these are not revised and edited to make the language more universal, they will confuse and frustrate nontechnical readers.

Be sure to approach revising and editing in a disciplined way. Read and reread your drafts, keeping your audience and purpose in mind. Look to make improvements in many ways: perhaps in data sets, in explanations of processes or theories, in vocabulary, and in the sequencing of paragraphs that build up a picture of how work was developed.

The activities at this stage in the writing process can be divided into large-scale revising, small-scale revising, and editing. Work from the large scale to the small.

## ▌LARGE-SCALE REVISING

### REVISING CONTENT

Reread your first draft to look at the content—all the big stuff. Consider these sorts of questions.

- Did I get all the data?
- Do I need to pull in another chart to show how we decided which geographic areas required the installation of seismic monitoring equipment?
- Does my reader need further explanation of coppice growth to understand why we eliminated some of the collected specimens in our species survey?
- Did I explain too much when I included an overview of the signal-processing steps in a digital radio receiver?

Questions of content are most important. They have the greatest impact on the readability of your document. Your reader will be troubled if you provide too much or not enough detail. Do not spend too much time discussing unimportant aspects and neglect what is most significant. Misplaced emphasis hides what you know from your reader.

Review your first draft to ensure that you followed your outline. This review can reveal the need for modifications that will ensure a logical, balanced sequence of information. "Shall I introduce this operating principle before the data, or shall I introduce the data and add the explanation afterwards?" Adding, subtracting, and re-ordering sections of content are the most significant improvements that you can make to your paper.

---

SAMPLE TECHNICAL TEXT WITH ERRORS

*The following example is from the first draft of a student paper on magnetic surveying in archaeology. It is an excerpt from the first main section after the introduction. It contains many errors that will be discussed and corrected later in this chapter.*

### THEORY OF MAGNETISM

#### Principle of Earth Magnetism

The magnetic field of the earth, which is roughly analagous to a tremendous dipole magnet, and which can be defined at any point on the earth in terms of three elements declination, dip, and intensity. The earth's magnetic field also varies continuously if measured at any one place as a result of transient variations such as those induced by magnetic storms, so a magnetized needle which is allowed to freely pivot in all directions will point at different angels both vertically and horizontally according to the place and the time of the observation. Magnetometers are used to measure magnetic fields in the earth. The practical unit used to measure magnetic intensity (field strength) is the gamma to measure small variations in intensity. Clay contains iron oxides such as magnetite which are said to be ferrimagnetic in that they possess a net magnetic moment in the absence of a magnetic field. Thus, each particle of such minerals can behave like a compass needle. Clay contain metallic particles the alignment of which is random and which are held in place by the structure of the clay. Heated clay, as during the firing of pottery or bricks, the magnetic particles become free to move. The tempature above is the Curie point, that is, the temperature above which a magnetic mineral loses its magnetism. If the clay is allowed to cool freely, the metallic particles will be affected by the earth's magnetic field at the place in which the cooling occurs. Thus, the particals will become magnetized in the direction in which the earth's field is pointing at that time. The magnetism, called thermo-remnant magnetism, will remain fixed in the clay unless it is reheated past the Curie point or subjected to a very strong nearby magnetic or electric field. A wide range of magnetization will occur in clays due to the proportions of ferrimagnetic minerals, the temperature of baking, and the magnetic field strength in which the clay was cooled.

Not only is clay a component of pottery and bricks but also of the kilns wheere these objects are fired. In that the kilns usually remain in their original location, this phenomenon has an implication in the dating of sites. The remnent magnetism, especially that of kilns, can be related to time with respect to the dip and direction of the magnetic field. Ely comparison with other objects having the same magnetic alignments, it is possible to establish relative chronologies. The theory of archaeomagnetism was first developed in 1899. Not until 1933 were studies begun in an effort to build up histories of local veriations in the earth's magnetic field. Magneticdating relationships have now been established as far back as 4000 B. C. E.

---

## ADDING CONTENT

Review your descriptions of specific content.

- Are they complete?
- Are the details accurate?
- Do any of these descriptions need graphic support?

These additions can be significant. A first draft often lacks many of the details that are important to technical readers in order for them to understand often complex subject matter that demands attention to detail.

## ADDING DEFINITIONS

Definitions of scientific, engineering, and technical concepts can be significant aids to your reader's understanding. In the revised and edited sample text (see page 58), for example, definitions of *declination, dip*, and *intensity* have been integrated into the first paragraph so that the general science reader, for whom this paper is intended, will be able to understand the physical variables that are being measured.

In the sample text, note that the additional information for the definitions comes from a research paper, a secondary source written by Aitken et al. Note also that an appropriate citation—in this case, in CSE name-year format—has been appended to the definitions to indicate the source of information.

## ADDING EXPLANATIONS

Additions from secondary sources to illustrate, define, or corroborate your descriptions are also useful. Explanations of concepts and processes can help a nontechnical reader understand better. This support is especially important when the reader's ability to process and understand later descriptions and discussion in the text depend on a prior grasp of concepts, procedures, processes, or situations.

In the sample text, an addition to the definition of *intensity* in the first paragraph makes the reader aware of factors that influence variations in intensity. Since this information comes from a secondary source—Wilson, 1995—another citation has been added to acknowledge this source.

## SHORTENING PARAGRAPHS AND ADDING HEADINGS

Long paragraphs containing two or more points risk losing the reader's attention. Shorter paragraphs focus your reader's attention on one point at a time to allow more complete absorption of the information on first reading. Short paragraphs (50–70 words) should alternate with longer paragraphs (75–125 words) as needed.

Break text into shorter units between headings.

If a long paragraph becomes a series of shorter ones, give the sequence its own heading.

For example, the first paragraph in the sample text ends with the discussion of magnetic intensity because the description of earth magnetism is now complete (see page 58). The next topic—ferromagnetic clay—is the logical place to begin a new paragraph.

The new paragraph is also the beginning of a new general topic area—thermo-remnant magnetism—so it is the place for a new subheading within the general text.

## ADDING SIGNIFICANT DETAIL

Adding smaller, specific detail of interest to the technical reader confirms identifications of samples and provides information that can be of practical use to the technical professional later on. For example, the revised sample text now includes the chemical formula for magnetite ($Fe_3O_4$) and the specific temperatures for the Curie point and for the firing of pottery. Although not essential to the description, such detail provides a more complete explanation of the natural processes being described.

Citations of sources, missed in the first draft, have also been added. (See page 58.)

## ADDING GRAPHIC COMMUNICATION

Graphic communication is essential to technical communication. Look for sections of your draft document that would benefit from a chart, table, diagram, or photograph: an explanation of a natural process, an illustration of a procedure, a graph showing temperatures at various pressures, and the like.

In the sample text, a significant addition is the diagram showing the re-alignment of the magnetic components of clay (see page 58). Note that this visual presentation, inserted at this exact point, helps the reader to understand the text description better.

Notice also that adding a figure requires adding an appropriate title block. In this case, the block includes the required figure number and title, an explanation of the keys to diagrams (a) and (b), and a citation because the diagram is borrowed from a printed source; also a reference to the figure is inserted at the appropriate place in the text: (see Figure 1). The figure appears immediately after the paragraph with the text reference so that the reader does not have to search for it.

## DELETING CONTENT

Technical readers want you to get to the point. Review your draft again and consider these sorts of questions.

- Have I said too much? Can I say this shorter?
- Will my audience already understand this technique or that scientific principle?
- Does my audience need to know this?
- Does this content fulfill the purpose of this paper?

In one of his letters, French philosopher and scientist Blaise Pascal apologized for the letter's length. He said that he would have written something shorter, but he did not have the time. Take the time to make your paper shorter. It will be better.

In the revised and edited example, descriptions of the earth's core and its magnetic field no longer appear: they were omitted from the sample text because they did not advance the purpose of the paragraph, namely, to describe the three properties of earth magnetism. The comments about the use of magnetometers and the first date for the theory of thermo-remnant magnetism were omitted for the same reason.

## ■ SMALL-SCALE REVISING: STYLE

In this phase of the revising and editing process, review your draft for the following:

- transitional words and phrases within paragraphs to make relationships clearer
- transitional paragraphs to connect text sections with previous ones
- specific examples to help readers better understand general principles
- wordy phrases and explanations that can be reduced or omitted

## PARAGRAPHS

Each paragraph develops one main point, stated in the topic sentence.

The inspection of footings revealed serious flaws.

If the paragraph contains parts, make the topic sentence an overview.

The shoreline reconstruction was completed in three phases: preparing the site, assembling riparian materials, and erecting new structures.

Each sentence that follows the topic sentence supports it with detail and explanation. Act on one or more of the following options:

- Define key terms.
- List steps in a procedure or stages in a process.
- Provide examples, including graphic support.

- Identify causes or factors.
- Define effects or implications.
- Defend assertions.

Each main point in your narrative should follow logically from the previous point. This flow creates the coherence essential to your reader's understanding of your text.

Connect each paragraph to the preceding paragraph with some form of logic: space, time, causality, example, and so on. The main points expressed in paragraphs do not have to be equally important, but they do have to relate to each other within their section of text. Connections can be made with appropriate referential language—adverbs and pronouns—and with transitional phrases and sentences.

> The mixer/amplifier is narrow banded. <u>Consequently,</u> it is used in intermediate frequency stages.

Bear in mind that long paragraphs are hard to read. Newspapers and magazines arrange text in short paragraphs, only two or three sentences each, to make text easier to scan. Readers pause between paragraphs, not between sentences. It is especially important, then, to break descriptions of complex scientific relationships and processes into the smallest possible components for the reader of scientific and technical literature. Each component can be expressed in a single, short paragraph.

Vary paragraph lengths to suit your purpose. Follow a longer paragraph that deals with a complex point with a short paragraph that makes a simple point or a transition to the next point.

## TRANSITIONS FOR COHERENCE: PARAGRAPHS

Transitions create coherence. They are the glue that holds diverse facts and ideas together in a consistent whole. They helped the reader make sense of the text as a whole.

Ensure that each new section in your document has a short, strong introductory paragraph that connects the next section of the text to the previous one. Each transitional paragraph summarizes the previous section and sets out the design of the section to come.

As an example, in the boxed sample text with errors above, the initial mention of earth magnetism comes at the beginning of the main body of the report; therefore, no need to summarize the report's introduction applies. However, the mention is quite short so a paragraph is needed to complete the discussion of earth magnetism and link it with the paper's purpose, to discuss magnetic surveying techniques used in archaeology. The transitional paragraph appears within the revised version on page 58.

## TRANSITIONS FOR COHERENCE: WORDS AND PHRASES

Transitional phrases and words within paragraphs express common logical relationships and give paragraphs coherence. Draw on the following options to make logical connections between ideas for your reader:

- addition: *also, moreover, in addition*
- comparison: *likewise, similarly*
- contrast: *although, however*
- illustration: *for example, in other words*
- cause and effect: *because, consequently, therefore*
- time and space: *before, when, above, north*
- summary: *finally, to summarize*

Some repetition of key words and phrases that express essential content will also promote coherence and provide appropriate emphasis.

Pronoun references are of particular concern to the technical writer striving for coherence. Where a pronoun can refer to two or more potential antecedents, the reader can easily misinterpret.

> The planting crew each night planned the next day's site work. It was estimated to cost 125 man-hours.

Is it the planning or the site work that cost the man-hours? Removing the ambiguous pronoun in favour of a specific reference will clarify the meaning.

> The planting crew each night planned the next day's site work.
> The planning time cost 125 man-hours during the four-month contract.

## SENTENCE LENGTH AND STRUCTURE

The more nontechnical the intended reader, the shorter your sentences should be. Several formulae are available to help assess readability. Most of these take into account the number of words per sentence and the number of syllables per word. Popular texts, such as newspapers and magazines, are easy to read because the publishers and editors aim for shorter words, sentences, and paragraphs. At the other extreme, doctoral theses, with long words and sentences, are hard to read; they are not aimed at a general audience.

Aim for moderately difficult readability in technical communication. Some longer words in technical literature will be necessary to express precisely the meaning intended. Some longer sentences will be necessary to describe more complex technical ideas or processes. Review your draft for long sentences that can be revised into shorter ones, but not extremely short ones that force repetitions of key words. Ending a sentence at the logical end of a complete thought allows your reader to pause and absorb the point before reading the next.

Make sentence structure strong and simple. The normal assertive sentence in English begins with the subject and predicate, followed by modifiers where necessary. Subject-first is the strongest structure in English and best able to carry the weight of detail necessary in technical writing.

## THE PASSIVE VOICE IN TECHNICAL COMMUNICATION

### THE PASSIVE VOICE DEFINED

What is the passive voice? Consider this sentence in the active voice: *The boy hit the ball.* In the passive voice, it would read: *The ball was hit by the boy.* The passive voice makes the object of the active sentence, *ball*, into a sentence subject, thereby focusing the reader's attention on the object and relegating the active element, *boy*, to a phrase modifier, *by the boy.*

With the passive voice, the active element can even be eliminated because it has become a modifier, something unnecessary to the grammar of the sentence: *The ball was hit.*

Do not confuse the passive voice with the past tense. Passive is not about past time. It defines a relationship between the subject and predicate of a sentence.

### THE PASSIVE VOICE: PROS AND CONS

Controversy surrounds the use of the passive voice in technical writing. Some argue that technical communication requires the passive voice.

- It preserves necessary objectivity by keeping the experimenter and the human factor out of the discussion.

- In the corporate world, it is often safer to avoid responsibility, as in *It was decided that we continue with the current policy.*
- Using *I* and *we* as sentence subjects is too informal for professional documents.

Others argue that the universal use of the passive is neither necessary nor desirable. Objectivity lies in the design of the experiment, not in the language used by the experimenter. With a little creative thought, writers can determine sentence subjects other than *I* and *we*.

### HOW TO USE THE PASSIVE VOICE

The best practice is balance. A universal application of the passive voice will deaden writing as readers struggle to translate. A limited and appropriate use of the passive voice is a reasonable choice.

The passive voice is appropriate to emphasize results, rather than the person responsible for those results. In most descriptions, this person—experimenter, technician, installer, surveyor, customer service engineer—is less important to the audience and purpose than the results.

> Elevated turbidity was noted at all stations sampled in the lake as measured with the Secchi disk.

Note in this next example that the sense of the sentence could still be expressed in the active without mentioning the experimenter.

> All stations sampled in the lake exhibited elevated turbidity as measured with the Secchi disk.

The active voice is appropriate for instructions.

> Install an in-line fuse holder into the line cord as close as possible to the battery terminal.

Passive and active voices can be combined to focus your reader on specific content. If you want to describe the process of getting saw logs to the mill, keep the logs in the subject, using both active and passive: "The logs float into the mill pond and are hauled up to the mill by a chain conveyor."

Alerts for sentences in the passive voice are defaults in the grammar checkers of most word-processing software. Do not conclude from this that sentences in passive voice are wrong, only that caution is required in using them. Default values for passive voice constructions can be altered or removed if the alerts distract you or if you need to set a limit to the number of passives used in a paragraph of your text.

## SENTENCE TYPES

Vary your sentence types. Mix long with short and offset with medium lengths. Mix simple sentences with complex or even compound-complex sentences. Determine sentence length according to your content. Readers prefer variation.

Check your work for repetition of sentence construction. If you frequently introduce sentences with long phrase or clause modifiers, restructure some with the modifiers at the end. *Before adding the catalyst and observing any reactive products in the resulting solution, check the temperature of the parent mixture* would become *Check the temperature of the parent mixture before adding the catalyst and observing any reactive products in the resulting solution.*

Strong sentences begin with the subject and predicate. Ensure that most of your statements are subject-first sentences.

## WORDY PHRASES

Check your drafts for wordy phrases. Can anything be cut without losing meaning? Does each sentence get to the point quickly, using strong nouns and verbs?

Eliminate needless repetition in the form of different words with similar meanings or words that repeat meanings already implicit in the language. An example of the latter is *past history*; history is the study of the past; *past* is needless repetition. Many wordy phrases creep into the first draft from common speech where they have a social function not required in the written language.

In the edited sample text on page 58, expression has been tightened to get to the point faster and make it more economically, without violating the required precision of technical language or omitting essential ideas.

## DIRECTNESS

Be brief and direct. As you compose a first draft, extra words and phrases from everyday speech will creep in; as you revise, eliminate them in favour of shorter, more direct ones.

Get to the point. Some points will be difficult to frame in words. Use the words you can think of and then rewrite. Experiment with vocabulary, phrasing, and sentence structure until they express exactly what you mean in as few words as possible.

Don't write the way you talk. Some will tell you to, but a conversational tone is contrary to the professional tone expected by your audience. We talk in a loose, associative babble that is ill suited to the precision required of technical communications. We use far more words in speaking than we need in order to communicate exact meaning. These extra words have a social function, but are superfluous in the written language.

# ▌EDITING

## CORRECT LANGUAGE

Editing is making your language follow the rules so that your message can be understood by the widest possible audience easily and without distraction. Language mistakes block the reader from understanding the content. They obstruct the process of decoding what you are saying and bring confusion. The following are some of the dimensions of language to check for correctness.

### DICTION

Diction is your choice of words. Keep diction simple and straightforward. Know the terms commonly used in your professional field and use them with the appropriate audience. A general audience will consider them jargon.

- Avoid over-using adverbs and adjectives. A *big 50 MW transmitter* is repetitive. A transmitter putting out 50 MW of radio frequency is big; there is no need to add a descriptive word that repeats the idea. Trust your nouns and verbs; they are the strongest words in English. Choose them well, and they will carry your meaning to the audience.
- Change pompous language that uses long words to shorter, more direct English. Instead of *necessitate*, say *need*. Instead of *expenditure*, say *cost*. Governments and corporate bureaucracies often produce this kind of needlessly ornate language.
- Technical language must be precise. Is the *connector* a plug, a fastener, or a link? Does the verb *insert* require the assembler to push, drop, slide, or roll the unit into place?

- Avoid negatives. Instead of writing *Be careful not to test voltages at the diode junction too often*, say, *Be careful to test voltages at the diode junction only when output from the final amplifier exceeds 150 milliamps*. Negatives accumulate in the reader's mind. They can obscure your meaning and wear the audience down until they stop reading. Positives will energize a reader to keep reading.

## SPELLING

Buy a current dictionary of Canadian English and use it. A good investment, a dictionary will prove useful for many years. Always check words that tickle your mind and leave you unsure of their spellings, meanings, pronunciations, or parts of speech.

Keep a personal dictionary of technical terms you need. Be sure to include their meanings and spellings. Include common words that you misuse and have to check frequently in the dictionary. Writing them out helps you to learn them.

Canadian English uses some U.S. and mostly British spellings. Canadians write in Canadian English.

# CONVENTIONS OF TECHNICAL WRITING

Technical communications contain more measured quantities and compound words for technical terms than do other types of communications. A technical writer must learn conventional ways of writing numbers, abbreviations, and hyphens in the text of a document. Note the following conventions used in technical writing.

## THE USE OF NUMBERS

- Write quantities as numerals when combined with specific units of measurement.

  300 pfd    210 mg/l

- Write quantities of 10 or greater as numerals. If no other rule applies, write quantities of fewer than 10 in words.
- Write all quantities in a series, or list of items in a sentence, as numerals.

  . . . capacitance values of 5 mfd, 3500 mfd, and 4700 mfd

- Use numerals for the time of day (*6:30 p.m.*), the day of the month (*November 21*), money (*$151.69*), decimal expressions (*3.1416*), and percentages (*73.8%*).
- Never begin a sentence with a numeral. Either write out the quantity in words or recast the sentence so that the quantity appears later.
- In compound number adjectives, write out the first number or the shorter number and use numerals for the other.

  sixty-four 0.625-in. rebar (No. 5)

## THE USE OF ABBREVIATIONS

- Abbreviate units of measurement that follow an exact, measured quantity.

  147.161 MHz    924 mW

- Write abbreviations in the singular: *5000 rpm*, not *rpms*.
- Write abbreviations in lower case, with the exceptions of abbreviations of proper nouns or those capitalized by convention.

  1500 Btu    150 mA

- Symbols may be used instead of abbreviations in some cases.

  54° north latitude     46%

- Form abbreviations for compound terms and names of organizations (acronyms and initialisms) by writing the first letter of each significant word.

  CSWA for Canadian Science Writers' Association     HTML for Hypertext Markup Language
  JPEG for Joint Photographic Experts Group

## THE USE OF HYPHENS

Write prefixes solid with the root word (*predetermined, outsource*), except for the following which require the use of hyphens:

- Hyphenate for internal capitals, as in *all-Canadian*.
- Hyphenate to aid pronunciation (e.g., *co-worker*).
- Hyphenate the prefix *self-*: *self-regulating, self-directed, self-inductance*.
- Hyphenate compound adjectives, but not compound nouns: *aluminium-alloy substrate* (substrate made of aluminum alloy).
- Hyphenate letter-word compounds.

  I-beam    A-frame    S-curve

- Observe dictionary spellings and hyphenate accordingly.

# THE VALUE OF GRAMMAR

This handbook provides the essentials to identify and correct problems with your use of the English language in your drafts.

The dimensions of English syntax are many and complex. Take a simple phrase like *between you and I*, commonly heard in speech. The pronoun *I* is incorrect because it follows the preposition *between*. Prepositions require the objective forms of the nouns and pronouns that follow them as objects. Thus the correct phrase is *between you and me*.

Some technical writers think they do not have to learn rules of grammar and usage, yet find that significant portions of their technical communications fail to reach their intended readership.

Think of it this way. The language that precisely describes words and word functions is just like the specialized vocabulary you use to discuss benthic organisms or nanotechnology. Just as the precise vocabulary of science and technology is essential to the scientist, engineer, and technologist, the vocabulary of language function and usage is essential for the writer, bringing precision, flexibility, and clarity to the work of writing. Writers who know how the language functions produce better work.

We want language to be transparently simple, and it isn't. It's like cell phone technology. We turn on the phone, dial the number, and talk. But how many people understand the sophisticated circuits in the phone, let alone the bewildering communications network that they access when they turn their phones on? We don't have to know the technology in order to use it, just as your reader doesn't have to know grammar to understand you. But you, the writer, have to understand it in order to create the system of words and phrases that will make sense to the widest reading audience.

Understanding grammar is worth the effort. As you learn the vocabulary of grammar, the parts of the sentence will begin to make sense to you and open new possibilities for expressing your ideas and information clearly and concisely. Dip back into this book frequently. Look for the structures discussed in these sections in your own work and reading. You will begin to recognize the underlying patterns of English and will learn to use them effectively. Doing this is not exciting, but it is as necessary as having a foundation for a house; miscommunication costs time and money.

The following is the section of the sample paper on magnetic surveys in archaeology after it has been revised and edited. Compare the two passages (see page 49 for the draft). Notice how much easier the second version is to read and understand.

---

THEORY OF MAGNETISM

### Principles of Earth Magnetism

The magnetic field of the earth, which is roughly analogous to a tremendous dipole magnet, can be defined at any point on the earth in terms of three elements: declination, dip, and intensity. Declination, the horizontal component, is the angular deviation of magnetic north from true north. Dip is the vertical angle through which a freely suspended magnetic needle dips from the horizontal. Magnetic dip is latitude dependent and varies from 0° at the magnetic equator to 90° at the magnetic poles. Intensity, the vertical component of the magnetic field, increases from the equator to the poles (Pumpernickel et al., 1981: 9). The earth's magnetic field also varies as a result of transient variations such as those induced by magnetic storms or magnetic anomalies in the crust (Wilson 1995: 139). The practical unit used to measure magnetic intensity (field strength) is the gamma (T) to measure small variations in intensity (Pumpernickel et al., 1981: 11).

### Principles of Thermo-remnant Magnetism

Clay contains ferromagnetic iron oxides, such as magnetite ($Fe_3O_4$), which possess a net magnetic moment in the absence of a magnetic field. Each particle in such minerals can behave like a compass needle. Clay contains metallic particles with random alignments held in place by the structure of the clay. Heating clay during the firing of pottery or bricks frees the magnetic particles to move.

The Curie temperature is the temperature above which a magnetic mineral loses its magnetism. The Curie point for most metallic minerals is from 580 to 680°C. Pottery is usually fired at temperatures up to about 800°C. If the clay is allowed to cool freely, the metallic particles will be affected by the earth's magnetic field at the place in which the cooling occurs. Thus, the particles will become magnetized in the direction in which the earth's field is pointing at that time (see Figure 1). The magnetism, called thermo-remnant magnetism, will remain fixed in the clay unless it is reheated past the Curie point or subjected to a strong nearby magnetic or electric field. A wide range of magnetization will occur in clays due to the proportions of ferromagnetic minerals, the temperature of baking, and the magnetic field strength in which the clay was cooled (Pumpernickel et al., 1981: 16–18) (Wilson 1995: 139–141).

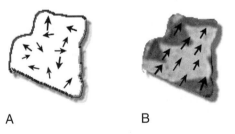

A                    B

**Figure 1.** Domain alignment in clay (Aitken et al., 1981: 18). (a) Unbaked clay: Domains are in random directions and net magnetic effect is small. (b) Baked clay: Elevated temperatures allow preferential alignment of domains which subsequently remain fixed at normal temperatures.

---

Clay is a component of pottery, bricks, and kilns where these objects are fired. Because the kilns usually remain in their original location, the presence of thermo-remnant magnetism in the clay allows the archaeologist to measure the age of a site where clay is present. By measuring the direction of the thermo-remnant magnetism in large clay objects like kilns, the archaeologist can place the site on a timeline of charted variations in the dip and direction of the earth's magnetic field and establish an absolute date.

In 1933, a series of scientific studies began to develop histories of local variations in the earth's magnetic field, especially the movements of the magnetic poles. Magnetic dating relationships have now been established as far back as 4000 BCE (Wilson 1995: 142).

# FINISHING YOUR DRAFTS

## PUT IT AWAY

When you think you have produced a good piece of work, put it away for a day or week. Take a walk. Start a new project. Then, return to your document with a cool objectivity and see clearly what is working and what is not.

## EXTERNAL REVIEW

Get help with your best drafts. Ask the person you trust most as a reader to read your manuscript before you submit it: perhaps your reviewer will be a colleague at work, a friend with knowledge of your subject, or a willing office assistant. Choose a constructive critic who will be honest in appraising your work—it is time to hear the worst; then, cut out the weak material and rewrite the rest.

Second and third drafts will likely be shorter than the first.

## REWRITING

Rewrite. Then rewrite again. Each time you read through your manuscript, look for passages that can be expressed better: explanations that are too long and can be shortened, a written procedure that would benefit from a simple visual, text that needs more precise use of language to make a point clearly. Keep rewriting.

## THE QUALITIES OF GOOD TECHNICAL COMMUNICATION

When you revise and edit, check that you have the qualities that your audience looks for:

- *Precision:* Be precise in your choice of words and phrases to convey technical concepts. Ensure accuracy in your use of technical concepts, "getting the technology right," working to understand scientific principles and relationships completely before expressing them in words.
- *Clarity:* Make simple, direct sentences. Technical concepts and processes are complex and lead to complex syntactical structures in sentences and paragraphs, making them difficult for the reader. Do not begin sentences with long phrase or clause modifiers. Use recognizable sentence patterns, such as definitions or technical descriptions.
- *Coherence:* Use transitional words and phrases that clarify connections and relationships between points.

- *Appropriateness:* Use language appropriate for your audience and purpose. Technical terms should be appropriate for the technical level of your intended audience. If you are not sure what that level is, define terms used and perhaps provide a glossary.
- *Conciseness:* Make it short. Eliminate the kind of "filler" language used in speaking socially. Instead of *due to the fact that,* write *because.*
- *Directness:* Do not digress. Get to the point and express it briefly. Write content connected to the idea you have stated in the topic sentence of your paragraph or in the opening paragraph of a document section.

---

**SAMPLE PASSAGE TO ILLUSTRATE DESIRABLE QUALITIES**

The flow of electrical current can induce the migration of impurities or other defects through the bulk of a solid. This process is called electromigration. In simple electromigration, the force on the defect is thought to have two components. The first component is the force created by direct interaction between the effective charge of the defect and the electric field that drives the current. The second component, called the "wind force," is the force caused by the scattering of electrons at the defect.

Stroscio and Eigler, 1991

---

# FORMATTING

## CHOOSING AN APPROPRIATE FORMAT

After a rigorous process of revising and editing your text, you will need to put the text in a form dictated by audience and purpose. It is beyond the scope of this handbook to review all the possible forms your document might take; however, a campus format manual, a company manual for formatting technical reports, or a published guide to formatting technical documents will help you to resolve these issues.

Most documents are subject to the following conventions.

## MANUSCRIPT FORM

- Use 8 ½ by 11 white paper of 20 lb. quality; the metric equivalent is 20 cm by 30 cm, found in some Canadian government departments. Choose a printer that gives a clean image. Use the default page margins set in your word-processing software. Double-space your manuscript. Indent the first line of each paragraph.
- Use a standard typeface, such as the serif Times Roman or Garamond, or sans serif Arial or Universe.
- Number pages in the upper right corner, except for the first page.
- Present your manuscript appropriately. Informal presentation can be pages stapled in the upper left corner. More formal presentation includes envelopes or report covers, each carrying a label with at least the title, author(s), destination (submitted to), and date. Fly pages with corporate logos and spiral binding can be part of formal presentations for long reports.

# FRONT AND BACK MATTER

The following are the pages of front and back matter found in formal reports. Choose the ones appropriate for your report presentation.

Front Matter

- title page
- memo or letter of transmittal
- table of contents
- list of illustrations (tables and figures)
- abstract

Back Matter

- references
- glossary
- appendix(es)

# CHECKLIST FOR REVISING AND EDITING YOUR DOCUMENT

Before you submit your final draft, have you

- budgeted adequate time for revising and editing?
- avoided procrastinating?
- revised the content, adding significant detail?
- revised the content, eliminating unnecessary detail?
- checked for transitional words, phrases, and paragraphs?
- written a strong topic sentence in each paragraph?
- checked each paragraph for coherence and details that support the topic sentence?
- broken long paragraphs into shorter, more readable ones?
- varied paragraph length to suit your purpose?
- written short transitional paragraphs to connect sections of your text?
- checked for clear, logical, appropriate words and phrases?
- checked your pronoun references?
- improved readability by shortening sentences and paragraphs?
- checked your sentence structure for subject-first?
- kept to a limited and appropriate use of the passive voice?
- varied your sentence types?
- checked your draft for wordy phrases?
- made your points briefly and directly?
- checked your diction for the correct choice of words?
- checked your diction for appropriate technical language?
- avoided pompous or needlessly technical language?
- made technical terms precise?
- checked your spelling?
- checked your use of numbers, abbreviations, and hyphenations?
- checked your grammar and usage with the rules in this handbook?
- given your draft to a colleague or editor for review?
- given your draft a final check for precision, clarity, coherence, appropriateness, conciseness, and directness?
- sought guidance from your audience concerning the expected final format of the communication?

The following explains common errors made by technical writers. Refer to these sections when editing your work or responding to questions and suggestions about your use of language. If you discover that you have a tendency to make any one of these errors with some frequency, review the relevant section and practise the correct forms. Doing so will improve your sense of grammar for the next piece of writing you complete.

## ■ SENTENCE FRAGMENTS

### DEFINITION AND EXAMPLES

A sentence is one complete independent clause that contains a subject and verb. A sentence fragment, on the other hand, is part of a sentence that is set off as if it were a whole sentence: it starts with a capital letter and sometimes ends with a final period or other end punctuation. However, the fragment lacks essential requirements of a grammatically complete and correct sentence. The fragment may, for example,

1. lack a verb

   Just Phil and I.

2. lack a subject

   Pacing the hallway.

3. be a subordinate clause commencing with a subordinating word

   When I fly a kite.

Sentence fragments give readers a fragment of a thought as opposed to a complete thought, and they interfere with writing clarity. Sentence fragments are serious writing errors, and they must be eliminated.

## TESTING FOR SENTENCE FRAGMENTS

Fragments can be spotted easily when they appear in isolation, but are more difficult to identify when they are near complete sentences. If you suspect a group of words is a sentence fragment, consider the following:

- Does the word group have a verb?
  - ❑ YES.   Consider the next question.
  - ❑ NO.   *The word group is a fragment. Revise it to include a verb.*
- Does the word group have a subject?
  - ❑ YES.   Consider the next question.
  - ❑ NO.   *The word group is a fragment. Revise it to include a subject.*
- Does the word group start with a subordinating word, making it a subordinate clause?
  - ❑ YES.   The word group is a sentence fragment. Revise it to create a complete sentence.
  - ❑ NO.   If you answered yes to the two previous questions and no to this one, the word group is a complete sentence and does not require revision for sentence completeness.

Make sure to consider all three questions when reviewing your sentence, because a fragment could be missing more than one essential sentence element. If your evaluation indicates that you have a sentence fragment, use the following strategies to transform it into a complete sentence.

## ELIMINATING SENTENCE FRAGMENTS

To fix the sentence fragment and make it a complete sentence, do one of the following:

1. Attach the sentence fragment to an independent clause, or a clause that contains the essential element lacking in the fragment (e.g., a subject or a verb).

   Just Phil and I <u>were pacing</u> the hallway.

2. Compose an independent clause from the fragment.

   At the emergency ward, <u>the parents were</u> pacing the hallway.

3. Drop the subordinating word.

   ~~When~~ I fly a kite.

## SUBORDINATE CLAUSES

A subordinate clause contains a subject and a predicate, or verb, but the clause begins with a subordinating word or phrase, such as *after, although, if,* or *until,* or a relative pronoun, such as *that, which, what, who.* Therefore, the clause is not independent.

You can make a subordinate clause into an independent clause in one of two ways:

1. Merge the subordinate clause with a nearby sentence.

They delineated a larger 2,028,224 ha rectangular study area that included the

*because*

Romeo Malette Forest (RMF) in Northeastern Ontario. ~~Because~~ the larger area minimized the impact of edge effects on their results.

2. Delete the subordinating element of the clause.

They delineated a larger 2,028,224 ha rectangular study area that included the Romeo Malette Forest (RMF) in Northeastern Ontario. ~~Because~~ The larger area minimized the impact of edge effects on their results.

## PHRASES

A phrase is a group of words that does not have either a subject or a verb and therefore cannot stand alone as an independent clause or sentence. Look at these examples:

to go kayaking

for the umpteenth time

with great trepidation

Major types of phrases include noun phrases, adjective phrases, adverb phrases, and prepositional phrases.

## FIXING PHRASE FRAGMENTS

You can address phrase fragment problems in two ways:

1. Incorporate the phrase into a nearby sentence.

Your company library and online database has an array of industry

*, which is there for*

resources. ~~For~~ every employee to use.

As a researcher into the paranormal, he took part in the

*, a*

smudging. ~~A~~ ceremony using smoke to purify the psychic energy field, or aura, around a person.

2. Turn the phrase into a complete sentence by adding a subject, predicate (verb), or both.

Smokejumpers land with heavy gear, including two parachutes, puncture-proof Kevlar suits, freeze-dried food,

*The jumpers are followed by* *containing*

fire shelters, and personal effects. ∧ cardboard boxes ~~heaved out of the airplane are~~ chain saws, shovels, and axes that ∧

*are heaved out of the airplane.*

## OTHER WORD GROUPS

Other commonly fragmented word groups include

- compound predicates
- examples introduced by *for example, such as,* and *for instance*
- lists

The following section will help you identify these fragmentation problems and provides strategies for correcting them.

## COMPOUND PREDICATES

The predicate is the part of the sentence that contains the verb. It indicates what the subject is doing or experiencing, or what is being done to the subject. A **compound predicate** contains two or more predicates with the same subject.

Joel wanted to buy a new computer and printer. ~~But~~ [but] could afford to purchase only a used laptop.

## EXAMPLES INTRODUCED BY *FOR EXAMPLE, SUCH AS,* AND *FOR INSTANCE*

You will often need to introduce examples, illustrations, and explanations to support arguments and ideas in your technical writing. Some common words and phrases used to introduce examples, illustrations, and explanations include the following:

*also, and, as an illustration, besides, but, equally important, especially, for example, for instance, furthermore, in addition, in particular, including, like, mainly, namely, or, specifically, such as, that is, to illustrate*

Sometimes, a fragment introduced by any one of the above words or phrases can be attached to the sentence before it to create a complete sentence.

Data rates that are limited to 10's of megabits per second are offered by conventional wireless data networks. ~~Such~~ [, such] as Bluetooth or IEEE 802.11.

However, in some instances you may find it necessary to change the fragment containing examples into a new sentence.

The Web allows information to be communicated in many ways. ~~For~~ [; for] instance, [a web designer can] ~~showing~~ [show] diagrams, ~~animating~~ [animate] processes, ~~linking~~ [link] web pages, or ~~using~~ [use] flashing red capitals on a blue background.

## FRAGMENTS IN LISTS

Occasionally, list elements are fragmented. This type of writing problem usually can be corrected by using a colon or dash.

During my rare vacations, I work on my three R's. ~~Reading~~ [: reading], rest, and running.

# ACCEPTABLE FRAGMENTS

Professional writers may use sentence fragments intentionally for emphasis or effect.

*Forming Transitions*
Now for the con side.

*Answering Questions*
And should we go along with this position? Under no circumstances.

*Advertising*
Proven effective.

Many instructors and editors do not accept sentence fragments, even intentional ones, in formal writing. Fragments may be acceptable in less formal writing contexts, such as an informative e-mail or an article for a company newsletter. Even in contexts where they are permitted, do not over-use sentence fragments.

## ■ COMMA SPLICES AND FUSED SENTENCES

Incorrectly joining two or more independent clauses within a sentence is a writing error. An independent clause, or main clause, contains at least a subject and a verb, and the clause can stand on its own as a separate grammatical unit. When two independent clauses appear in a single sentence, they must be joined in one of two ways:

1. using a comma and one of the seven coordinating conjunctions: *and, but, for, nor, or, so, yet*
2. with a semicolon or other acceptable punctuation such as a dash or a colon

Fused sentences (also known as run-on sentences) or comma splices occur when two independent clauses are incorrectly joined within the same sentence.

### COMPARING FUSED SENTENCES AND COMMA SPLICES

In a fused sentence, no punctuation or coordinating conjunction appears between the two independent clauses.

independent clause                    independent clause
[Canada's most famous ship is the *Bluenose*] [it was originally designed to fish and race.]

In comma splices, the independent clauses are joined (or spliced) with commas and without a coordinating conjunction.

Canada's most famous ship is the *Bluenose*, it was originally designed to fish and race.

Writers often use conjunctive adverbs in place of coordinating conjunctions and, in so doing, create comma splice errors. A coordinating conjunction is one of these seven words: *and, but, or, nor, for, so,* and *yet.* A conjunctive adverb, on the other hand, is a word such as *furthermore, however,* or *moreover.* However, merely placing the word *however* and commas between two independent clauses does not correct a comma splice error.

*Comma Splice Involving Conjunctive Adverb*
*Incorrect:* Canada's most famous ship is the *Bluenose,* however, it was originally designed to fish and race.

### IDENTIFYING FUSED SENTENCES OR COMMA SPLICES

Use the following checklist to determine whether a sentence is fused or is a comma splice.

- The sentence contains two independent clauses.
  - ❏ NO.   Neither of the errors applies.
  - ❏ YES. *Proceed to the next question.*
- The independent clauses are joined by a comma and a coordinating conjunction.
  - ❏ YES.  The clauses are correctly joined.
  - ❏ NO.   *Proceed to the next question.*
- The independent clauses are joined by a semicolon or other acceptable punctuation, such as a colon or a dash.
  - ❏ YES.  The clauses are correctly joined.
  - ❏ NO.   *Use one of the revision strategies provided in the next section to correct the fused sentence or comma splice.*

## STRATEGIES FOR CORRECTING FUSED SENTENCES OR COMMA SPLICES

You have four major options for correcting fused sentences or comma splices:

1. Add a comma and a coordinating conjunction: *and, but, for, nor, or, so, yet.*

   Canada's most famous ship is the *Bluenose,* yet it was originally designed to fish and race.

2. Add a semicolon or other appropriate punctuation, such as a colon or a dash.

   Canada's most famous ship is the *Bluenose;* it was originally designed to fish and race.

   OR

   Canada's most famous ship is the *Bluenose;* however, it was originally designed to fish and race.

3. Revise the sentence to subordinate one of the clauses.

   Even though Canada's most famous ship is the *Bluenose,* it was originally designed to fish and race.

4. Turn each independent clause into a separate complete sentence.

   Canada's most famous ship is the *Bluenose.* It was originally designed to fish and race.

## REVISION WITH A COORDINATING CONJUNCTION

A comma must precede the coordinating conjunction *and, but, for, nor, or, so,* or *yet.*

It was −30° C with a wind-chill factor ⟨, but⟩ we still installed the anemometer as planned.

The neutralizing agent is called "titrant" ⟨, and⟩ the amount of titrant used reflects the original oxygen concentration in the sample.

## REVISION WITH A SEMICOLON OR COLON

Use a semicolon without a conjunction if the relationship between the two independent clauses is clear.

The overflow assures that when the sample bottle is closed, the cone inside the cap will push excess liquid out; no air will be trapped inside.

Use a semicolon and a comma with independent clauses that are joined with a conjunctive adverb or transitional phrase, such as

*also, as a result, besides, consequently, conversely, for example, for instance, furthermore, in addition, in fact, meanwhile, moreover, nonetheless, next, on the other hand, otherwise, similarly, subsequently, then, therefore, thus*

The liquid will turn cloudy; then, a precipitate will form as chunks or solid flakes.

Use a colon if the first independent clause introduces the second.

The requests are thorough and varied: a chicken or rabbit will be skinned, boned, quartered, shredded, turned into patties, prepared for stew, the liver for this, the kidney for that.

## REVISION BY REDUCING SENTENCES TO PHRASES AND CLAUSES

This option for correcting fused sentences and comma splices is usually the most effective since it provides the most revision choices and clarifies idea relationships.

You will first need to decide which of the independent clauses you would like to emphasize.

~~Swirl~~ *Swirling* the vial , slowly press the plunger until the sample solution is less blue.

The rules of hockey , developed in the 1870s, ~~they~~ stipulated , *that* there be nine players on a team instead of six as there are today.

*Because there* ~~There~~ is a smog alert in south-central Ontario, people with breathing difficulties are advised not to go outside.

## REVISION BY SEPARATING SENTENCES

Because the clauses in fused sentences and comma splices are independent, they can stand on their own as separate grammatical units.

Thoroughly rinse the titration vial with distilled water . *Discard* ~~discard~~ in a waste bucket.

The fixed sample is orange, . A a nearly full syringe of titrant is needed.

# PROBLEMS WITH PRONOUNS

A pronoun is a word that replaces a noun or another pronoun. Three major types of pronoun problems occur frequently in writing:

1. antecedent agreement problems
2. reference problems
3. case problems:
   a) personal pronouns
   b) whether to use *who* or *whom* in sentences

## PRONOUN–ANTECEDENT AGREEMENT

The antecedent is the word the pronoun replaces. If the antecedent is singular, the pronoun that refers to it will also be singular.

The <u>microbiologist</u> will first adjust <u>his or her</u> microscope on a sample slide.

Similarly, if the antecedent is plural, the pronoun will be plural.

We add <u>reagents</u> to the sample bottle because <u>they</u> form a chemical complex between free oxygen molecules and some of the particulate matter in the water sample.

Indefinite pronouns do not refer to any specific person, thing, or idea:

*another, anybody, anyone, anything, each, either, everybody, everyone, everything, neither, nobody, none, no one, nothing, one, somebody, someone, something*

In formal English, treat indefinite pronouns as singular even though they may seem to have plural meanings.

Anyone familiar with the Hawthorne effect should anticipate contamination of the management of patients in one arm of the trial by his or her *[not their]* management of patients in the other arm.

## CORRECTING INDEFINITE-PRONOUN AGREEMENT PROBLEMS

1. Change the plural pronoun to a singular, such as *he* or *she*.

   When the airplane hit severe turbulence, everyone feared for
   *his or her*
   ~~their~~ safety.

2. Make the pronoun's antecedent plural.

   *the passengers*
   When the airplane hit severe turbulence, ~~everyone~~ feared for their safety.

3. Recast the sentence to eliminate the pronoun agreement problem.

   *safety was a common fear among all those on board.*
   When the airplane hit severe turbulence, ~~everyone feared for their safety.~~

Because the use of *his or her* can be awkward and wordy, especially if used repeatedly, consider correction strategies 2 and 3 as preferable alternatives.

## GENERIC NOUNS

A **generic noun** names a typical member of a group, such as a typical classroom teacher, or a typical dentist. Generic nouns might appear to be plural; however, they are singular, and any pronouns referring to them must also be singular.

Each Olympic athlete must sacrifice if he or she plans [not *they plan*] to win a gold medal.

## COLLECTIVE NOUNS

A collective noun names a group of people or things. Examples of collective nouns include the following words:

*audience, army, choir, class, committee, couple, crowd, faculty, family, group, jury, majority, number, pack, team*

### IF THE COLLECTIVE NOUN REFERS TO A UNIT
Use the singular pronoun.

The audience stood and applauded to show its approval.

### IF PARTS OF THE COLLECTIVE NOUN ACT INDIVIDUALLY
Use a plural pronoun.

The audience folded their collapsible chairs and placed the seats in a storage room.

Often it is a good idea to emphasize that the antecedent is plural by adding a word, such as *members*, describing individuals within the group.

The audience members folded their collapsible chairs and placed the seats in a storage room.

MAINTAIN SINGULAR OR PLURAL CONSISTENCY

Whether you treat the collective noun as singular or plural, ensure that you consistently treat references within the sentence as singular or plural, respectively.

*has*
The faculty ~~have~~ completed its review of courses for the upcoming term.

## COMPOUND ANTECEDENTS

TWO OR MORE ANTECEDENTS JOINED BY **AND**

Antecedents joined by *and* form a compound antecedent and require a plural pronoun whether the antecedents are plural or singular.

Dave and Michaela were starving after their [not *his and her*] day of skiing in Whistler.

TWO OR MORE ANTECEDENTS CONNECTED BY **OR, NOR, EITHER . . . OR, NEITHER . . . NOR**

Make the pronoun agree with the nearest antecedent.

Either Melodie or the Chans will have their way.

*Note:* With a compound antecedent such as the one above, place the plural noun last to prevent the sentence from sounding awkward.

Neither the captain nor the other players could explain their lopsided defeat.

# PRONOUN REFERENCE

A pronoun is a word that replaces a noun or another pronoun. Using pronouns allows you to avoid repeating nouns in speech and writing.

Once Jarod tested the graphic accelerator board, he installed it in the computer.

However, when the relationship between the antecedent and the pronoun is ambiguous, implied, vague, or indefinite, your intended meaning becomes unclear and may be completely lost to the reader.

## AVOIDING AMBIGUITY ABOUT PRONOUN REFERENCE

When it is possible for a pronoun to refer to either one of two antecedents, the sentence is ambiguous.

*1*          *2*
*Ambiguous:* Franz told his father that his car needed a new transmission.

To eliminate the ambiguity, either repeat the clarifying antecedent or rewrite the sentence.

*Option 1:* Franz told his father that his father's car needs a new transmission.

*Option 2:* Franz said to his father, "Dad, your car needs a new transmission."

## AVOIDING IMPLIED ANTECEDENTS

The reader should be able to clearly understand the noun antecedent of any pronoun you use. This antecedent must be stated and not implied or merely suggested.

Before the raging fire spread too close to nearby farms, ~~they~~ *the residents* were ordered to leave their homes.

Make sure that antecedents refer to nouns present in, or near, the sentence.

In ~~Hirsch and Kafka's~~ *Hirsch and Kafka* work on burn probability, ~~they~~ *their* apply a model that predicts when and where fires might occur.

## AVOIDING VAGUENESS THROUGH THE USE OF THE PRONOUN ANTECEDENTS *THIS, THAT, WHICH,* AND *IT*

Pronouns *this, that, which,* and *it* should refer clearly to specific noun antecedents, not to large groups of words expressing ideas or situations.

The access points to the network, the wireless terminals, become bottlenecks for high data-rate applications; this *"last-mile" problem* is compounded by the effects of multipath in the wireless channel which makes high data-rate transmission difficult.

A spot forecast may state that a temperature range for a specific canyon in the forest will be between 25 and 30 degrees, the humidity between 12 and 14 percent, and the winds 15 km an hour. ~~This interests~~ *All of these data interest* firefighters.

## AVOIDING INDEFINITE USE OF *IT, THEY,* OR *YOU*

Do not use the pronoun *it* indefinitely; for example, "In this book [article, chapter, and so on] it says . . ."

~~In~~ Chapter 23 of the textbook ~~it~~ states that hydroacoustic technology is a cost effective way to quickly perform fish population surveys and determine bottom topography in large bodies of water.

Never use *they* without a definite antecedent.

If an air bubble is present, ~~they~~ *the technicians* take another sample from the creek.

In formal writing, the use of *you* is acceptable when you are addressing the reader directly.

If <u>you</u> do not want the beeper on, select OFF, and if <u>you</u> want it loud, select HIGH.

In formal writing, do not use *you* as an indefinite pronoun.

To mitigate the DC offsets, ~~you AC-couple~~ *one AC-couples* the baseband amplifiers to the output of the RF mixers.

# PRONOUN CASE (*I* VS. *ME*, ETC.)

Case refers to the form a noun or pronoun takes according to the function of that noun or pronoun in a sentence. In English there are three cases:

1. The subjective case indicates that the pronoun functions as a subject or a subject complement.
2. The objective case indicates that the pronoun functions as the object of a preposition or a verb.
3. The possessive case indicates that the pronoun shows ownership.

| PRONOUN CASES | | |
| --- | --- | --- |
| SUBJECTIVE | OBJECTIVE | POSSESSIVE |
| I | me | my |
| we | us | our |
| you | you | you |
| she/he/it | her/him/it | her/his/its |
| they | them | their |

## USING THE SUBJECTIVE CASE

The subjective case (*I, we, you, she/he/it, they*) must be used when the pronoun functions as a subject or as a subject complement.

*As a Subject*
Tony and I split the cost of the video.

A subject complement is a noun or adjective that follows a linking verb and renames or describes the sentence subject. Because the use of pronouns in the subjective case sounds quite different from the way you might use pronouns in informal speech, subjective case pronouns as subject complements frequently create writing difficulties.

*As a Subject Complement*
*Correct:* The students who did the most work are Ivan and she.

*Incorrect:* The students who did the most work are Ivan and her.

In all formal writing, ensure that you use the subjective pronoun case when the pronoun is part of the subjective complement.

The woman Anatole married is she.

If the construction sounds too unnatural, you may wish to recast the sentence.

She is the woman Anatole married.

## USING THE OBJECTIVE CASE

Use an objective case pronoun (*me, us, you, her/him/it, them*) if the pronoun functions as

1. a direct object

   The foreman asked him to read the WHMIS sheet.

2. an indirect object

   The company foreman gave Sam and me our hard hats.

3. the object of a preposition

   Just between you and me, the highpass filter is a better solution.

## USING PRONOUNS IN COMPOUND SUBJECTS AND OBJECTS

A compound subject or a compound object includes more than one pronoun.

*Compound Subject*
She and I did the inspection of the footings.

*Compound Object*
The new park master plan surprised her and me.

The fact that the subject or object is compound does not affect the case of the pronoun. However, a compound structure often causes a writer to confuse pronoun case.

To determine whether you have selected the correct pronoun case, try mentally blocking out the compound structure except for the pronoun in question. Then decide whether the pronoun case you have selected is correct.

*Incorrect:*
~~My two field staff members and~~ me

*Correct:*
~~My two field staff members and~~ I

did the driving.

After checking the position of the forms, the engineer gave the
job of filling the forms with concrete to Robert and ~~I~~ *me*.

In spite of our difficulties, my partner and ~~me~~ *I* finished the job on time.

Avoid using a reflexive pronoun such as *myself* or *himself* when you are uncertain about the pronoun case.

The footing forms were designed by a qualified engineer and ~~myself~~ *me*.

## USING PRONOUNS AS APPOSITIVES

An appositive is a noun or noun phrase that renames a noun, noun phrase, or pronoun. When a pronoun functions as an appositive, it has the same function, and hence case, as the noun or pronoun that it renames.

Three members of the field crew—Clara, Michael, and
~~me~~ *I*—found an extensive manganese deposit.

Let's you and ~~I~~ *me* take the weekend off and go to the West Edmonton Mall.

## USING THE CORRECT PRONOUN CASE WHEN *WE* OR *US* PRECEDES A NOUN

Sometimes, you may need to decide whether *we* or *us* should come before a noun or noun phrase. Mentally block out the noun so that only the pronoun remains. Then decide which pronoun case is correct.

*Correct:*
We ~~forest managers~~

*Incorrect:*
Us ~~forest managers~~

plan timber harvesting.

Follow the same procedure when considering pronouns that function as sentence objects.

us
The lead engineer signals to ~~we~~ crane operators during loading procedures.

## MAKING COMPARISONS USING *THAN* OR *AS* WITH PRONOUNS

When making comparisons using *than* or *as*, writers frequently leave out words that are clearly understood by readers.

John Sawyer is more qualified as a rigger <u>than</u> I ~~am qualified~~.

## USING THE POSSESSIVE CASE TO MODIFY A GERUND

A gerund is a form of a verb that ends in -*ing* and is used as a noun; for example, *Fencing is my favourite sport*. Use a pronoun in the possessive case (*my, our, your, her/his/its, their*) to modify a gerund or gerund phrase.

his
The inspector did not approve of ~~him~~ using Marr connectors at the junction box.

Possessive nouns can also modify gerunds.

The crew's pumping of toxic waste took 30 hours of non-stop clean-up operation.

# *WHO* AND *WHOM*

*Who* and *whom* are pronouns. *Who* is the subjective case; it must be used only for subjects and subject complements. *Whom* is the objective case; it must be used only for objects.

1. *Who* and *whom* are used as interrogative pronouns to open questions.
2. As relative pronouns, *who* and *whom* are used to introduce subordinate clauses.

## AS INTERROGATIVE PRONOUN TO OPEN QUESTIONS

To decide whether to use *who* or *whom*, you must first determine the pronoun's function within the question. Does the interrogative pronoun function as a subject or subject complement, or as an object?

Who
~~Whom~~ ordered the truck mixers for the bridge construction project?

Whom
~~Who~~ did the human resources manager interview?

## AS RELATIVE PRONOUN TO INTRODUCE SUBORDINATE CLAUSES

Use *who* and *whoever* as relative pronouns for subjects, and use *whom* and *whomever* for objects. When deciding which pronoun to use, you must determine whether the relative pronoun functions as a subject or object within the subordinate clause. A good technique to employ when making this decision is to mentally block off the main clause and focus on the subordinate clauses you are considering.

whoever
Logging the well is the responsibility of ~~whomever~~ owns the drilling contact.

whom
We don't know ~~who~~ the CIO nominated to chair the committee.

Do not be misled by interrupting expressions, such as *I know, they think,* or *she believes,* which often come after *who* or *whom* in a subordinate clause.

The contractor allows on site only employees ~~whom~~ *who,* I think, have been certified in safety procedures.

# SUBJECT–VERB AGREEMENT

Every sentence has a subject (stated or implied) and a verb. Subject–verb agreement refers to the relationship between the subject and the verb.

In the present tense, verbs must agree with subjects in two ways:

1. In number: Number means the subject can be singular (e.g., *I*) or plural (e.g., *we*).
2. In person: Person can be first person (*I, we*), second person (*you*), or third person (*she, he, it,* or *they*).

If the verb is a regular verb and the subject is in the third-person singular, use the *-s* (or *-es*) form of the verb.

<u>Tony</u> works for his godfather.

| PRESENT-TENSE FORMS OF *WORK* | | |
|---|---|---|
| | SINGULAR | PLURAL |
| FIRST PERSON | I *work* | we *work* |
| SECOND PERSON | you *work* | you *work* |
| THIRD PERSON | she/he/it *works* | they *work* |

Notice how the following irregular verbs achieve subject–verb agreement.

| PRESENT-TENSE FORMS OF *DO* | |
|---|---|
| I *do* | we *do* |
| you *do* | you *do* |
| he/she/it *does* | they *do* |

| PRESENT-TENSE FORMS OF *HAVE* | |
|---|---|
| I have | we have |
| you have | you have |
| he/she/it has | they have |

The verb *to be* has different forms for the present and past tenses.

| PRESENT-TENSE FORMS OF *BE* | |
|---|---|
| I *am* | we *are* |
| you *are* | you *are* |
| he/she/it *is* | they *are* |

| PAST-TENSE FORMS OF *BE* | |
|---|---|
| I was | we were |
| you were | you were |
| he/she/it was | they were |

Often, if you have been speaking or writing English for a long time or know the language well, problems with subject–verb agreement will be obvious to your ear or eye. For example, the sentence *Jamie look good in his tuxedo* immediately sounds or looks incorrect. It is obvious that the subject and verb do not agree. The sentence should begin *Jamie looks good....*

However, some subject–verb agreement problems are more difficult to spot. A number of English sentence constructions make the subject difficult to identify—often the subject is located far from the verb—and, as a result, it is easy to make subject–verb agreement mistakes. Information in the following section will help you to avoid the most common subject–verb agreement problems.

## WORDS BETWEEN SUBJECT AND VERB

Occasionally, the modifying words between the sentence subject and verb include a noun, which might be mistaken for the subject. As a result, some writers use a verb that does not agree with the real subject.

When evaluating any sentence for subject–verb agreement, mentally delete any modifying elements, such as prepositional phrases, so that only the sentence subject and verb remain. Then assess whether or not the subject and verb agree. You might consider drawing an arrow to connect the subject with the verb, as has been done in the following example.

The <u>first 10 minutes</u> on an oil rig *are* the most frightening.

The <u>workers</u> on an offshore rig ~~practises~~ *practise* emergency drills for three hours every week.

The <u>objective</u> in written sets of instructions ~~are~~ *is* the proper and safe performance of the procedure.

Phrases beginning *along with, as well as, in addition,* and *together with* do not change the number of the subject because they are not part of the subject.

The finished bridge <u>abutment,</u> along with the crane barges and their crews, *was photographed* for the company newsletter.

## SUBJECTS WITH *AND*

A compound subject contains two or more independent subjects joined by *and*. The compound subject requires a plural verb.

These <u>pumps, cylinders, and control valves</u> *were* designed for hydraulic systems on heavy mobile equipment.

The power amplifier's PSK modulation <u>scheme and</u> the vector modulator's variable phase shift <u>network</u> ~~has~~ *have* given the transmitter architecture simplicity and stability.

However, when the parts of the subject refer to a single person or idea, they require a singular verb.

<u>Bacon and eggs</u> *is* a breakfast favourite.

<u>Kick and sweep</u> *has* been used to collect freshwater benthic organisms from streams for environmental assessment.

The pronouns *every* and *each* are singular, and require singular verbs, even if the subjects they precede are joined by *and*.

Every <u>woman</u> and <u>man</u> has a right to a safe workplace.

## SUBJECTS WITH *OR* OR *NOR*

When a compound subject is joined by *or* or *nor*, make the verb agree with the part of the subject nearer to the verb.

Neither the engineer nor his technologists *know* whether the substrate under the footings is saturated.

Either the structural engineers or the crane operator *has* the authority to stop all construction work on the bridge.

## INDEFINITE PRONOUNS

An indefinite pronoun does not refer to a specific person or thing. The following are indefinite pronouns:

*all, anybody, anyone, anything, each, either, everybody, everyone, everything, neither, no one, nobody, none, nothing, one, some, somebody, someone, something*

Although many indefinite pronouns seem to refer to more than one person or thing, most require a singular verb. Note especially that *each, every,* and words ending in *-body* and *-one* are singular.

Everybody on the project *was* working 12-hour shifts.

*takes*
Each driller on the rig ~~take~~ responsibility for safety.

### NEITHER AND NONE

When used alone, the indefinite pronouns *neither* and *none* require singular verbs.

Neither *is* correct.

Of the employees who were sent to repair the rig, none *has* been seriously injured.

When prepositional phrases with plurals follow the indefinite pronouns *neither* and *none*, in some cases a plural or singular verb may be used. However, it is best to treat *neither* and *none* consistently as singular.

Neither of those regulations *applies* to this project.

None of these projects *requires* government approval.

### INDEFINITE PRONOUNS THAT CAN BE SINGULAR OR PLURAL

A few indefinite pronouns, such as *all, any, more, most, none,* and *some,* can be singular or plural, depending on the noun or pronoun to which they refer.

*Singular:* All of the money *is* in a company bank account.

*Plural:* All of his accounts *are* frozen because of a credit problem.

## COLLECTIVE NOUNS

A collective noun names a class or a group of people or things. Some examples of collective nouns are *band, committee, family, group, jury,* and *team.*

Use a singular verb with the collective noun when you want to communicate that the group is acting as a unit.

> The <u>crew</u> *agrees* that it needs a new supervisor.

> *has*
> The technical staff ~~have~~ a good safety record

Use a plural verb when you want to communicate that members of the group are acting independently.

> The <u>original crew</u> *have* gone on to find other jobs in the industry.

> The technical staff *have* completed <u>their mandatory fitness tests.</u>

Sometimes, it is better to capture the idea of individual action by recasting the sentence with a plural noun.

> The <u>original crew members</u> *have* gone on to pursue other careers.

### DECIDING WHETHER TO TREAT *NUMBER* AS A SINGULAR OR PLURAL

If the collective noun number is preceded by *the,* treat it as a singular noun.

> <u>The number</u> of ways to manage engine controls *is* increasing.

If *number* is preceded by *a,* treat it as a plural.

> <u>A number</u> of soil types *are* formed by physical and chemical weathering.

### UNITS OF MEASUREMENT

Use a singular verb when the unit of measurement is used collectively; that is, when the thing described by the noun cannot be counted.

> <u>One-half</u> of the water <u>sample</u> *is* treated with manganese sulfate solution.

Use a plural verb when the unit of measurement refers to individual persons or things that can be counted.

> Only <u>one-half</u> of the <u>specimens</u> *are* preserved in formalin for future use.

## SUBJECT AFTER VERB

Most often the verb follows the subject in sentences. However, in certain cases, the verb may come before the subject, making it difficult to evaluate subject–verb agreement.

### EXPLETIVE CONSTRUCTIONS

Expletive constructions include phrases such as *there is, there are,* or *it is, it was.* When these phrases appear at the beginning of a sentence, the verb often precedes the subject.

> There *are* significant <u>differences</u> among types of magnetometers.

## INVERTING SENTENCE ORDER

To achieve sentence variety, you may from time to time wish to invert traditional subject–verb order. Ensure that when you do this, you check that the subject and the verb agree.

*are*
Situated at the ends of the Lions Gate Bridge ~~is~~ the City of West Vancouver and Stanley Park.

## SUBJECT COMPLEMENT

A subject complement is a noun or adjective that follows a linking verb and renames or describes the sentence subject, as in *A pulaski is a hand tool for fighting forest fires.* Because of its relationship to the subject, the complement can often be mistaken for the subject and result in subject–verb agreement errors.

*is*
The manager's central <u>concern</u> ~~are~~ safety issues.

*are*
A <u>hydrophone and sonic tags</u> ~~is~~ all we need to track game species of fish.

## WITH RELATIVE PRONOUNS

The relative pronouns—*who, which*, and *that*—introduce adjective clauses that modify the subject. The relative pronoun must agree with its antecedent. The antecedent is the noun or pronoun to which the relative pronoun refers. Thus, the verb must agree with the antecedent.

The new <u>bridge</u>, which *carries* five lanes of northbound traffic, accommodates bicyclists, pedestrians, and future light-rail transit.

### CONSTRUCTIONS USING *ONE OF THE* AND *ONLY ONE OF THE*

Subject–verb agreement mistakes are often made with relative pronouns when the sentence contains *one of the* or *only one of the*.

Generally, with constructions using *one of the*, use a plural verb.

*measure*
The Suunto clinometer is *one of the* <u>kinds</u> of instruments that ~~measures~~ tree heights and diameters.

Generally, with *only one of the* constructions, use a singular verb.

The oval gear flow meter is *only* <u>one</u> *of the* positive displacement flow meters

*is*
that ~~are~~ used to measure flow in clean liquids.

## PLURAL FORM, SINGULAR MEANING

Some words ending in *-ics* or *-s* are singular in meaning, even though they are plural in appearance. These words include the following:

*athletics, economics, ethics, physics, politics, statistics, mathematics, measles, mumps, news, species*

Nouns such as the above generally require a singular verb.

*was*
Measles ~~were~~ causing the kindergarten class to miss school.

When nouns such as *mathematics, physics,* and *statistics* refer to a particular item of knowledge, as opposed to the collective body of knowledge, they are treated as plural.

Environment Canada <u>statistics</u> *reveal* that the area experienced record amounts of smog.

## TITLES AND WORDS AS WORDS

A work referred to by its title is treated as a singular entity, even if the title includes a plural word.

*establishes*
ISO Directives, Part 1: Procedures for the Technical Work ~~establish~~ international standards for technical work.

# ADVERBS AND ADJECTIVES

Adverbs and adjectives are modifiers. Adjectives modify nouns and pronouns. Adverbs can modify

- verbs

  He left the job site *early*.

- adjectives

  The operculum was *slightly* red.

- other adverbs

  They left the job site *very* late.

Many adverbs end in -ly (*walk* **quickly**); however, some do not (*walk* **often**). As well, some adjectives end in -ly.

The sea lamprey left an *ugly* gash on the trout's side.

Problems can occur when adjectives are incorrectly used as adverbs or vice versa. The best way to decide whether a modifier should be an adjective or an adverb is to determine its function in the sentence. If you are in doubt about whether a word is an adjective or an adverb, consult a current Canadian dictionary.

## ADVERBS

In modifying a verb, another adverb, or an adjective, an adverb answers questions such as the following: Why? When? Where? How? The following are some common misuses of adjectives in situations where adverbs are required:

1. incorrectly using adjectives to modify verbs

   *moderately   exactly*
   Torque through the drill is applied ~~moderate~~ and ~~exact~~ according to specifications.

2. incorrectly using the adjective *good* when the adverb *well* is required

*well*
The foreman indicated that the concrete pump performed ~~good~~ in all applications.

3. incorrectly using adjectives to modify adjectives or adverbs

*really*
The prototype radio uses a ~~real~~ high IF band centred at 17.35 GHz.

## ADJECTIVES

Adjectives usually come before the nouns they modify.

She watched the <u>red</u> dawn.

However, adjectives can also function as subject complements that follow a linking verb. The subject complement renames or describes the sentence subject.

Silence is <u>golden</u>.

Linking verbs communicate states of being, as opposed to actions.

*sour*
The milk at the back of the refrigerator tasted ~~sourly~~.

*happy*
She feels ~~happily~~.

*bad*
With storm clouds mounting, the weather looked ~~badly~~.

Some verbs, such as *look, feel, smell,* and *taste,* may or may not be linking verbs. When the word after the verb modifies the subject, the verb is a linking verb, and this modifying word should be an adjective. However, when the word modifies the verb, it should be an adverb.

*When the Modifier Is an Adjective*
The field assistant looked <u>curious</u>.

*When the Modifier Is an Adverb*
The field assistant looked <u>curiously</u> at the larvae under the log.

## COMPARATIVES AND SUPERLATIVES

Most adjectives and adverbs have three forms:

1. the positive
2. the comparative
3. the superlative

## FORMING COMPARATIVES AND SUPERLATIVES

### Adjectives

| POSITIVE | COMPARATIVE | SUPERLATIVE |
|---|---|---|
| **With one- and most two-syllable adjectives** | | |
| red | redder | reddest |
| crazy | crazier | craziest |
| **With longer adjectives** | | |
| intoxicating | more intoxicating | most intoxicating |
| selfish | less selfish | least selfish |
| **A few adjectives are irregular.** | | |
| good | better | best |
| bad | worse | worst |
| **Some have no comparative or superlative form.** | | |
| unique | — | — |
| pregnant | — | — |

### Adverbs

| POSITIVE | COMPARATIVE | SUPERLATIVE |
|---|---|---|
| **With adverbs ending in -ly** | | |
| selfishly | more selfishly | most selfishly |
| gracefully | less gracefully | least gracefully |
| **With other adverbs** | | |
| fast | faster | fastest |
| hard | harder | hardest |
| **A few adverbs are irregular.** | | |
| well | better | best |
| badly | worse | worst |
| **Some have no comparative or superlative form.** | | |
| really | — | — |
| solely | — | — |

## WHEN TO USE THE COMPARATIVE FORM
## AND WHEN TO USE THE SUPERLATIVE FORM

When comparing two entities, use the comparative form.

*lesser*

Which is the ~~least~~ of the two evils?

When comparing three or more entities, use the superlative.

Of the three options, the engineers felt that the suspended slab was the *best*.

Management strategies that strategically fragment forest landscapes are the

*most effective*

~~effectivest~~ to mitigate potential fire losses.

## DO NOT USE DOUBLE COMPARATIVES OR SUPERLATIVES

Of the two instruments, I feel that the version by Texas Instruments will last ~~more~~ longer.

Superheterodyne receivers have the ~~most~~ highest sensitivity and selectivity.

## DO NOT USE COMPARATIVES OR SUPERLATIVES WITH ABSOLUTE CONCEPTS

Absolute concepts by their very nature do not come in degrees and cannot be compared. Examples of absolute concepts are *favourite, unique, perfect, pregnant, impossible, infinite,* or *priceless.* If three diamonds are perfect, one cannot be more perfect than the other two.

*Incorrect:* The cat looked <u>more pregnant</u> than she did last week.

*Correct:* The cat's pregnancy was more obvious this week.

The bridge by-pass solution by the consulting engineers is ~~very~~ unique.

## DOUBLE NEGATIVES

Two negatives are acceptable in a sentence only if they create a positive meaning.

They were <u>not disappointed</u> with the results of the investigation.

A double negative is a non-standard English construction in which negative modifiers such as *no, not, neither, none, nothing,* and *never* are paired to cancel each other. Double negatives should be avoided in any formal writing.

The government never does ~~nothing~~ *anything* to solve the problem of high gasoline prices.

Do not put ~~no~~ *any* knives or other sharp tools in a tool box with blades exposed.

In standard English, the modifiers *barely, hardly,* and *scarcely* are considered negative modifiers. These words should not be paired with such words as *no, not,* or *never.*

They could ~~not~~ <u>barely</u> hear the warning siren.

## ◼ PROBLEMS WITH MODIFIERS

A modifier is a word, phrase, or clause that describes or limits another word, phrase, or clause within a sentence. Modifiers must be placed carefully and correctly; otherwise, they will cloud and, in some instances, destroy sentence meaning. Generally, modifying words should be kept close to the words they modify.

## LIMITING MODIFIERS SUCH AS *ONLY, EVEN*

Place limiting words such as *just, even, only, almost, hardly, nearly,* and *merely* directly before the verb they modify.

She <u>nearly</u> missed the bus to the job site.

If one of these words modifies another word in the sentence, place the modifier in front of that word.

*Incorrect:* Jacks can possibly, over time, sink down to the point that the rig might not <u>even</u> remain level <u>on asphalt</u>.

*Correct:* Jacks can possibly, over time, sink down to the point that the rig might not remain level, <u>even on asphalt</u>.

*Incorrect:* A large percentage of injuries occur to those employees who have <u>only</u> been on the job a short time.

*Correct:* A large percentage of injuries occur to those employees who have been on the job <u>only</u> a short time.

The modifier *not* is often misplaced, a situation that can create confusing or unintended meanings.

*Incorrect/Unintended Meaning:* All snakebites are <u>not</u> lethal.

*Correct/Intended Meaning:* <u>Not</u> all snakebites are lethal.

## MISPLACED PHRASES AND CLAUSES

A misplaced modifier is a describing word, phrase, or clause that is incorrectly positioned within a sentence, making the modifier's meaning illogical or unclear. The misplaced modifier relates to, or modifies, the wrong word or words in the sentence. When a modifier is misplaced, misreadings can result.

*Incorrect:* The staff technologists were told that they had been selected for the annual safety award <u>by the Industry Council</u>.

*Correct:* The staff technologists were told that they had been selected <u>by the Industry Council</u> for the annual safety award.

*Incorrect:* Walking to the job site on a subzero morning, <u>his left ear became frozen.</u>

*Correct:* Walking to the job site on a subzero morning, <u>he froze his left ear</u>.

Sometimes, modifier placement can cause the reader to misinterpret the writer's intention. The correction chosen will depend on the writer's intended meaning.

*Ambiguous:* The fellow we interviewed at the station <u>often</u> talked to us about the weather.

*Clear:* The fellow <u>we often interviewed</u> at the station talked to us about the weather.

*Clear:* The fellow we interviewed at the station <u>talked to us often</u> about the weather.

## AWKWARDLY PLACED MODIFIERS

Sentences should generally flow in a pattern from subject to verb to object. Keep the subject as close as possible to the main verb and, where possible, don't separate the subject from the main verb of the sentence with a modifying adverb clause.

*Awkward:* Processed film, <u>wound with the *START* target at the outer end</u>, will be delivered in accordance with ANSI/AIIM MS23-1991.

*Clear:* Processed film will be delivered <u>wound with the *START* target at the outer end</u> in accordance with ANSI/AIIM MS23-1991.

As well, keep auxiliary verbs near to the main verbs.

## SPLIT INFINITIVES

An infinitive consists of *to* and the verb, as in *to love, to leave,* and *to forget.* In a split infinitive, a modifier is placed between *to* and the verb. Frequently, a split infinitive will make a sentence awkward, and the sentence will need to be revised.

*Awkward:* Financial analysts expected the stock prices *to*, after a period of sharp decline, dramatically *rise*.

*Clear:* Financial analysts expected the stock prices *to rise* dramatically after a period of sharp decline.

*Awkward:* Try *to*, for this application, *use* an SHG blue laser.

*Clear:* Try *to use* an SHG blue laser for this application.

However, in a few instances, split infinitives are preferable to alternative wordings.

The acronyms and jargon that litter the Internet landscape fail *to* convincingly *convey* meaning because they're based on technical specifications with no immediately recognizable language roots: "TCP/IP," "MP3," and "KB," for example.

Generally, avoid split infinitives in formal writing.

## DANGLING MODIFIERS

A dangling modifier is a word, phrase, or clause that does not relate to any word within the sentence and, as a result, confuses the reader. Dangling modifiers usually appear at the start of the sentence and can be one of the following:

- a participial phrase

  <u>Limiting the discussion to technical specifications,</u> the benefits of new technologies for many individuals are not being realized.

- a gerund phrase

  <u>After building a new component</u>, clear written language is needed to document and market the product.

- an infinitive phrase

  <u>To make sure that no air bubbles are trapped inside,</u> an examination of the sample in the full dissolved-oxygen (D.O.) bottle is needed.

- an elliptical clause

  Fill the direct-reading titrator *(syringe)* with the titrant <u>until thick</u>.

To repair dangling modifier problems, use one of the following revision strategies:

1. Provide the subject of the sentence immediately after the dangling phrase.

   *Dangling Participial Phrase:* <u>Limiting the discussion to technical specifications</u>, the benefits of new technologies for many individuals are not being realized.

   *Correction:* Limiting the discussion to technical specifications, <u>we</u> are not realizing the benefits of new technologies for many individuals.

2. Provide a subject for the dangling phrase.

   *Dangling Gerund Phrase:* <u>After building a new component</u>, clear written language is needed to document and market the product.

   *Correction:* After building a new component, <u>we</u> need clear written language to document and market the product.

3. Revise the sentence by changing the subject.

*Dangling Infinitive Phrase:* <u>To make sure that no air bubbles are trapped inside</u>, an examination of the sample in the full D.O. bottle is needed.

*Correction:* To make sure that no air bubbles are trapped inside, (<u>you</u>) examine the sample in the full D.O. bottle.

*Elliptical Clause:* Fill the direct-reading titrator (*syringe*) with the titrant <u>until thick.</u>

*Correction:* Fill the direct-reading titrator (*syringe*) with the titrant until <u>the resulting solution is thick.</u>

To assess whether or not a sentence you have written has a dangling modifier, apply this questioning strategy:

- Does the participial phrase suggest an action without indicating who is performing the action?
  - ❏ NO.  You do not have a dangling modifier problem.
  - ❏ YES.  *Answer the following question.*
- Does the subject of the independent clause indicate who performs the action?
  - ❏ YES.  You do not have a dangling modifier problem.
  - ❏ NO.  *Apply one of the three strategies listed above to address the dangling modifier problem.*

## ◾ SHIFTS

A shift is a sudden and unnecessary change in point of view, verb tense, mood, or voice, or a change from indirect to direct questions or quotations. Shifts can occur within and between sentences. They often blur meaning and confuse readers.

### POINT OF VIEW

In writing, point of view is the perspective from which the work is written. It is often indicated by the pronouns the writer uses.

1. First person: *I, we*
2. Second person: *you*
3. Third person: *he/she/it/one* or *they*

You have probably noticed the following in the course of your own writing and reading:

- The first-person point of view often appears in more informal types of writing, such as journals, e-mails, and personal letters.
- The second-person point of view is often found in directions or instructional types of writing, such as this handbook.
- The third-person point of view emphasizes the subject. It is used in informative writing, including the writing you do in many academic and professional contexts.

Shifts in point of view occur when a writer begins a piece of writing in one point of view and then shifts carelessly back and forth to other points of view. To prevent needless shifts, think about the most appropriate point of view for your writing situation, establish that point of view in your writing, and keep to it.

*Shifts in Point of View*

Some people, when outfitting their dogs, will have them carry

*their*
their food. Thus, as ~~our~~ journey progresses, and stops are periodically made for meals or snacks, the dogs' packs become lighter.

Your fax machine supports both tone (or multi-frequency) and pulse (or rotary) dialling. It is initially set to **TONE**, so

*you do*                                         *you use*
~~one does~~ not need to change the setting if ~~he or she uses~~

that kind of line. If you are using a pulse dial line,

*you*
~~one~~ can change the setting to **PULSE** by following these steps.

A common problem among student writers is shifting from the third-person singular to the third-person plural or vice versa.

*Shift from Singular to Plural*

                                        *they prefer*
Since malamutes have very heavy fur coats, ~~it prefers~~ to sleep outside even in extremely cold weather.

## VERB TENSE

The verb tense tells the reader when the action in the piece of writing is taking place. Shifting from one verb tense to another without a sound reason confuses the reader.

*Tense Shift*

                                               *operates*
The transceiver IC represents a complete RF system. The transceiver ~~will operate~~

                                   *is*
in the 17-GHz frequency band and ~~be~~ fabricated in a SiGe BiCMOS process. The

*uses*
transceiver ~~will use~~ a direct conversion receiver and a vector modulator for transmission.

## VERB MOOD AND VOICE

### MOOD

Shifts can also occur in the mood of verbs. The mood of the verb indicates the manner of action. There are three moods in English:

1. The indicative mood is used to state facts or opinions, or to ask questions.

   Ridge forms used below grade stay in place.

   Is the footing form plumb and level?

2. The imperative mood is used to give a command or advice, or make a request.

   Use an inverted footing form as a funnel to pour the concrete into the system.

   Avoid dropping or placing heavy rocks or heavy wet soil on the footing form.

3. The subjunctive mood is used to express doubt, wishes, or possibility.

If an explainer or storyteller role were built into tech teams, the individuals in such roles could provide all the text describing a new product and its use.

## Mood Shift

Include more foreground than background by focusing closer than your main

*Include more background by focusing further than your main subject.*

subject while keeping the subject within the depth of field. ∧ ~~The reverse is also true.~~

## VOICE

Voice refers to whether a verb is active or passive. A verb is active when the subject is the doer of the action. A verb is passive when the subject of the verb receives the action. If the writer suddenly shifts between voices, it can be jarring and confusing to the reader.

*Shift in Voice*
I could comprehend the devastation of the avalanche as soon as

*I made*

∧ the turn opening to the valley ~~was made.~~

# INDIRECT TO DIRECT QUESTIONS OR QUOTATIONS

### DIRECT AND INDIRECT QUOTATIONS

In a direct quotation, the writer repeats a speaker's words exactly, placing those words within quotation marks. In an indirect quotation, the writer summarizes or paraphrases what the speaker has said.

*Direct Quotation:* Vice President of Operations Mike Smith said, "Our pumps and crews will place approximately 196,000 cubic yards of concrete into the bridge piers."

*Indirect Quotation:* Vice President of Operations Mike Smith says his pumps and crews will place approximately 196,000 cubic yards of concrete into the bridge piers.

**Shift from Indirect to Direct**

The shift inspector indicated that work is not to commence until the inspection

*that we must*

has been performed and ∧ correct any deficiencies noted during the inspection.

### DIRECT AND INDIRECT QUESTIONS

A direct question is a question that is asked directly.

What is differential levelling?

An indirect question reports that a question was asked, but does not ask it.

I asked what differential levelling was.

Shifting from indirect to direct questions can make writing awkward and confusing.

*Shift from Indirect to Direct*
I asked what differential levelling was and

*whether they knew*

~~did they know~~ how to use a level.

# ▮ MIXED CONSTRUCTIONS

A sentence with a mixed construction incorrectly changes from one grammatical construction to another, incompatible one, thereby confusing the sentence's meaning.

## MIXED GRAMMAR

When you draft a sentence, your options for structuring that sentence are limited by the grammatical patterns of English. You must consistently follow the pattern you choose within the sentence. You cannot start the sentence using one grammatical pattern and then abruptly change to another. *Don't switch horses* [grammatical structures] *in the middle of a stream* [sentence] is an idiom that can help you remember this key grammatical guideline.

> *Mixed:* When setting up on rough ground, two legs of the tripod set at about the same elevation.
>
> *Revised:* When setting up on rough ground, set two legs of the tripod at about the same elevation.
>
> OR
>
> *Revised:* When setting up on rough ground, two legs of the tripod should be set at about the same elevation.

Another mixed construction problem is incorrectly combining clauses.

> *Satellite*
> ~~Although satellite~~ dishes have become popular in many northern Canadian communities, but many viewers still prefer local stations.

From time to time, when revising your own work, you may encounter a sentence that can't be fixed grammatically. In instances such as this, it is often wise to rethink what you want to say and then recast the sentence so it is clear, straightforward, and logical.

> *Mixed:* As you are surveying switch operators occasionally to have simple hand signals to communicate the status of the measurement to the reflector person or the type of topography to the instrument person without having to shout or use two-way radios for simple communications.
>
> *Revised:* As you are surveying, switch operators occasionally, and use simple hand signals to communicate the status of the measurement to the reflector person or the type of topography to the instrument person, without having to shout or use two-way radios for simple communications.

## ILLOGICAL CONNECTIONS

A number of sentence faults can occur when elements of the sentence do not logically fit together. Faulty predication is one example of such a problem. In faulty predication, the subject and predicate do not make sense together. To remedy this problem, revise either the subject or the predicate.

> *Originally,*
> ~~The original function of~~ the Internet was created to exchange academic and military information.

The decisions on who would make Canada's 2002 Olympic

*were made*
hockey team ~~was chosen~~ by a management committee headed by Wayne Gretzky.

An appositive is a noun or noun phrase that renames or explains a noun or noun phrase immediately before it.

The total station, the theodolite with EDM capabilities, . . .

The appositive must logically relate to the noun or noun phrase that precedes it; otherwise, faulty apposition occurs.

*systems*
Bluetooth and IEEE 802.11 ~~engineers~~, conventional wireless data networks, offer data rates that are limited to tens of megabits per second.

## AVOIDING *IS WHEN, IS WHERE, REASON . . . IS BECAUSE*

In formal writing, avoid the following constructions:

1. is *when* or is *where*

   *In a forest management agreement,*
   ~~A forest management agreement is when~~ a provincial government grants a timber company rights to grow, harvest, and remove timber in return for long-term, sustained-yield timber management that takes into account social, economic, and environmental factors.

2. the *reason* . . . is *because*

   *We*
   ~~The reason we~~ scout the survey area first for suitable instrument stations ~~is~~ because time and precision may be lost with multiple setups.

These constructions are not grammatical and often add unnecessary words to a sentence. If you find such constructions in your drafts, revise the sentences that contain them.

## ◧ PARALLELISM

Parallelism in writing means that equal grammatical structures are used to express equal ideas. Errors in parallelism, known as faulty parallelism, occur when unequal structures are used to express equal ideas. Words, phrases, and clauses should all be parallel when they express a similar idea and perform a similar function in a sentence. When using parallelism for effect, balance single words with single words, phrases with phrases, and clauses with clauses.

*Parallel, Balanced Elements*
*Words:* There are three sides to every story—yours, mine, and all that lie between.

—*Jody Kern*

*Phrases:* Do what you can, with what you have, where you are.

—*Theodore Roosevelt*

*Clauses:* Think like a man of action, act like a man of thought.

—*Henri Bergson*

**Chapter 6** • Grammar

# WITH ITEMS IN A SERIES

When the reader encounters items in a series, he or she expects a parallel grammatical pattern to be maintained within the sentence. However, when one or more items do not follow the parallel grammatical pattern, the sentence seems jarring and awkward to the reader.

*Awkward:* The highest level of accuracy obtainable with GPS requires use of two units, one as a base station and the other visits the points of interest.

*Correction:* The highest level of accuracy obtainable with GPS requires use of two units, one as a base station and the other as a mobile station to visit the points of interest.

*Awkward:* Soil consistencies may be termed Soft, Medium Stiff (Medium firm), and Stiff (or firm), as well as quite Hard.

*Correction:* Soil consistencies may be termed Soft, Medium Stiff (Medium Firm), Stiff (Firm), or Hard.

*Awkward:* Being outdoors, feeling the winds off the ocean, and to smell the Douglas fir are what I like about hiking British Columbia's West Coast Trail.

*Correction:* Being outdoors, feeling the winds off the ocean, and smelling the Douglas fir are what I like about hiking British Columbia's West Coast Trail.

# WITH PAIRED ITEMS

Parallel ideas are often connected in one of three ways:

1. with a coordinating conjunction, such as *or, and*, or *but*
2. with a pair of correlative conjunctions, such as *not only . . . but also* or *either . . . or*
3. with comparative constructions using *than* or *as*

Whenever you relate ideas using one of these methods, always emphasize the connection between or among ideas by expressing them in parallel grammatical form.

## USING PARALLELISM WITH COORDINATING CONJUNCTIONS

Coordinating conjunctions are words such as *and, but, or, nor, for, yet*, and *so* that connect ideas of equal importance. Avoid faulty parallelism by ensuring that all elements joined by coordinating conjunctions are parallel in grammatical form.

*Not Parallel:* In practice, geodesy uses the principles of mathematics, astronomy, and applies concepts in physics.

*Parallel:* In practice, geodesy uses the principles of mathematics, astronomy, and physics.

*Not Parallel:* Contractors responsible for demolition work where an entire structure is razed will be required to certify that the levelled lot is filled to existing grade, to discontinue all service connections, capping all lines, and will submit signed documentation.

*Parallel:* Contractors responsible for demolition work where an entire structure is razed will be required to certify that the levelled lot is filled to existing grade, to discontinue all service connections, to cap all lines, and to submit signed documentation.

## USING PARALLEL FORMS WITH CORRELATIVE CONJUNCTIONS

Correlative conjunctions are pairs of words that join equal grammatical structures. Examples include *not only . . . but also, either . . . or,* and *both . . . and.* Avoid faulty parallelism by ensuring that each element linked by correlative conjunctions is parallel in its grammatical form.

*Not Parallel:* The staff of the computer lab not only supported the president's request for a bigger office, but also they were prepared to order a desk, a chair, and a bar for her convenience.

*Parallel:* The staff of the computer lab supported the president's request not only for a bigger office, but also for a desk, a chair, and a bar for her convenience.

*Not Parallel:* All your data in the form indicated in the raw data block needs to be changed to either be viewed by Liscad or as northing, easting, and elevation in Excel.

*Parallel:* All your data in the form indicated in the raw data block needs to be changed either to a format compatible with Liscad or to Excel format as northing, easting, and elevation data.

## COMPARISONS LINKED WITH *THAN* OR *AS*

You will often use *than* or *as* to make comparisons. To avoid faulty parallelism, make sure that the elements being compared are expressed using parallel grammatical structure.

*Not Parallel:* This fire management strategy is not as productive of more wildlife habitat as eliminating harvesting completely in some forest management units.

*Parallel:* <u>Implementing</u> this fire management strategy is not as productive of more wildlife habitat as <u>eliminating</u> harvesting completely in some forest management units.

*Not Parallel:* Rigid plastic footing forms are quicker and less expensive to install than conventional forming of concrete pier footings.

*Parallel:* Rigid plastic <u>footings</u> are quicker and less expensive to install than conventional concrete pier <u>footings</u>.

Note: The corrections shown above are just a few of many equally acceptable alternatives. In some instances, the corrections to faulty parallelism that occur to you may be improvements on the suggestions made here.

# STYLE

Some aspects of writing are matters of style, not of structure or of meaning. Here, there often are no hard-and-fast rules, but there are guidelines to help you streamline and clarify your writing to satisfy readers' needs and expectations. In this section you will find helpful advice to make your writing concise, direct, and persuasive.

## WORDINESS

Effective writing is concise, clear, and direct. Concise writing does not necessarily mean fewer words or shorter sentences. It means words that function clearly and sentences that express their point without empty words. A longer sentence is justified if it is required to express a sophisticated idea. On the other hand, many shorter sentences can be even more economically written. When revising, review each sentence you write with an eye to eliminating any phrase or word that is not absolutely necessary to your intended meaning.

### REDUNDANCIES

Redundancy, in this context, refers to unnecessary words in a sentence. Often, the same idea is expressed twice or more.

It is 6:30 ~~a.m. in the morning~~.

Other common redundancies include *final completion, important essentials, close proximity, consensus of opinion,* and *actual fact.*

A
~~The reason~~ a beam of sufficient power will not be reflected from an unprepared surface is because the power radiated from the total station is relatively low.

The board members did not want to repeat the debate ~~again~~, so they had a frank ~~and honest~~ discussion during which they identified some basic ~~essential~~ ideas.

When people are in ~~situations of~~ conflict at a meeting, they should

achieve
~~try to~~ attempt to ~~form a~~ consensus ~~of opinion~~.

The bridge ~~that people cross to get~~ to Burlington is ~~sort of~~ arched ~~in shape~~ and constructed of strong materials

and
such as structural steel~~,~~ ∧ reinforced concrete~~, and etc~~.

## UNNECESSARY REPETITION OF WORDS

Sometimes, you may wish to repeat words or phrases to create an effect or for emphasis, as in parallel constructions. However, when words are repeated for no apparent reason, they make writing seem sloppy and awkward. As you revise, eliminate unnecessary repeated words.

We observed ~~the stress responses of~~ four groups of benthic organisms to

they
determine whether ~~the groups of benthic organisms~~ differ in their responses to environmental stress and whether they could be early warning indicators for detecting

it
~~environmental stress~~.

The foundation ~~that the house sits on~~ is to be inspected before framing work begins or backfill is installed.

## EMPTY OR INFLATED PHRASES

Sometimes, to make your writing sound more important, you may be tempted to include certain phrases you have heard others use. When you examine your sentences carefully, you'll find these phrases only increase your word count and contain little or no meaning. Effective writers state what they mean as simply and directly as possible. As you revise your work, trim sentences of any empty or inflated phrases.

Because              currently
~~By virtue of the fact that~~ ∧ ~~at the current time~~ we lack sufficient funding, the skateboard park will not be built.

You can use concise words or phrases without affecting your meaning.

| ELIMINATING WORDY OR INFLATED PHRASES | |
| --- | --- |
| WORDY/INFLATED | CONCISE |
| along the lines of | like |
| as a matter of fact | in fact |
| at all times | always |
| at the present time | now, currently, at present |
| at this point in time | now, currently, at present |
| because of the fact | because |
| being that | because |

## SIMPLIFYING STRUCTURE

The following word-trimming strategies will help you make your sentences simple, clear, and direct.

### STRENGTHEN THE VERB

Nouns derived from verbs can often be turned back into verbs to make the sentence more direct and active.

The Casagrande device is used for ^ ~~the determination of~~ *determining* the liquid limit of soils.

### AVOID COLOURLESS VERBS

The verbs *is, are, was, were,* and *have* are weak and often create wordy sentence constructions.

~~Samples of benthic~~ *Benthic* ^ macroinvertebrates were ^ *sampled* in spring and either summer or autumn using a Surber sampler or by standardized kick-sampling with a handnet.

### REVISE EXPLETIVE CONSTRUCTIONS

An expletive construction uses *there* or *it* and a form of the verb *be* in front of the sentence subject. These constructions use unnecessary words. Remove the expletive and tighten the sentence to make it more concise and direct.

~~There is a process known as differential~~ *Differential* ^ positioning ~~that~~ measures to a set of satellites simultaneously from two receivers.

*Remaining is essential*

~~It is important that you should remain~~ ^ calm ^ if your kayak capsizes in rough water.

*Do a*

~~It is important that you should do a~~ ^ daily, pre-shift inspection of drilling equipment and its operating parts to maintain productivity and worker safety.

### WHERE POSSIBLE, USE THE ACTIVE VOICE

The active voice is generally more concise and direct than the passive voice. Use the active voice when you want to focus on the action of a sentence.

*Passive:* The research was conducted by a senior environmental engineer who was planning a constructed wetland project.

*Active:* A senior environmental engineer who was planning a constructed wetland project conducted the research.

## REDUCING CLAUSES AND PHRASES

Modifying clauses and phrases can often be tightened. Where possible, reduce clauses to phrases and phrases to single words.

An RFIC, ~~which is~~ a radio frequency integrated circuit, decodes the radio frequency signal and sends it to the intermediate frequency amplifier.

*The landmark*

~~Designated as a landmark structure, the~~ ^ bridge is located along transportation corridors important for emergency vehicles and the flow of economic goods.

# ■ DICTION AND AUDIENCE

The effectiveness of your writing will in large measure depend on the appropriateness of the language you decide to use for your audience. Choose the wording that best suits the context and the audience of your writing. Consider these elements as you choose your words:

- subject
- audience (their needs, expectations, and feelings)
- purpose
- voice (as reflected in your unique writing style)

The following section provides guidance and information that will help you to select appropriate language for the documents you write.

## JARGON

Jargon is the specialized language of a particular group or occupation. Writers of scientific or technical documents who work in specialized occupations may not be aware of the jargon they use daily as short forms of communication with other members of their profession. Such language—the specialized terms, the common words with specialized meanings, the short forms, the elliptical phrases and clauses—quickly loses an audience outside of the special group of professionals that uses it.

Technical writers contracted to write up needed documentation must learn the jargon of a specialized field and then find more common and universally understood words to express the same ideas for a nontechnical audience. Sometimes, they misunderstand the complexities and subtleties of the technology they are learning and writing about. It is better for people familiar with the science or technology to write about it, but they should also be aware of the jargon in their own speech.

In some instances, you may need to use jargon, such as when your audience is the particular group or in the occupation that uses the jargon, or when you can reasonably assume that your audience will understand this specialized language. Generally, though, avoid jargon and use plain English in its place.

*Jargon:* The DSP is now used in an asymmetric equalization scheme where data are pre-distorted on the downlink and post-equalized on the uplink back to the base station.

*Revised:* Wireless data from a base station computer is transmitted in a distorted signal to area laptop computers; the laptops correct the distortion and transmit an undistorted signal back to the base station.

In addition to specialized language, jargon often includes language that is intended to impress readers rather than to communicate information and ideas effectively. Jargon-filled language is often found in business, government, education, and military documents. Sentences containing jargon terms are difficult to read and extremely unclear.

*Jargon:* The Director of Instruction implemented the optimal plan to ameliorate poor test scores among reading-at-risk students.

*Clear:* The Director of Instruction carried out the best plan to improve poor test scores among students having trouble reading.

*Jargon:* We will endeavour to facilitate a viable trash recovery initiative for all residences in the neighbourhood.

*Clear:* We will try to create a workable garbage pickup plan for all neighbourhood homes.

If you encounter inflated words or phrases in your writing draft, consider alternative words that are simple, clear, and precise in meaning.

---

**ELIMINATING JARGON**

| WORDS DESIGNED TO IMPRESS | SIMPLE ALTERNATIVES |
|---|---|
| ameliorate | repair, improve, restructure |
| commence | begin, start |
| components | parts |
| endeavour | attempt, try |
| exit | go, leave |
| facilitate | help |
| factor | cause, consideration |
| finalize | complete, finish |
| impact on | affect |
| implement | carry out |
| indicator | sign |
| initiate | start, begin |
| optimal | best |
| parameters | boundaries, limits |
| prior to | before |
| prioritize | order, rank |
| utilize | use |
| viable | workable |

# EUPHEMISMS

A euphemism is a word or expression intended to take the place of harsher or more direct words or phrases. An example of a euphemism in a military context is *collateral damage*, a term sometimes used to describe civilian casualties. In a few writing situations, using euphemisms is acceptable. For instance, when expressing condolences to a friend you might use the euphemism *passed away* as a substitute for *died*. Generally, however, avoid euphemisms because they blur meaning and are highly indirect.

---

**AVOIDING EUPHEMISMS**

| EUPHEMISM | PLAIN ENGLISH |
| --- | --- |
| chemical dependency | drug addiction |
| correctional facility | jail |
| declared redundant | laid off |
| developing nations | poor countries |
| downsizing | laying off or firing employees |
| economically deprived | poor |
| effluent | sewage |
| ill-advised | very poor or bad |
| incendiary device | bomb |
| laid to rest | buried |
| leather-like | vinyl |
| mature | elderly, old |
| military solution | war |
| misleading phrase | lie |
| pre-owned automobile | used car |
| starter home | small house |
| strategic withdrawal | defeat or retreat |
| transfer station | temporary garbage dump |

---

# SLANG, REGIONALISMS, NON-STANDARD ENGLISH

## SLANG

Slang is the informal, colourful vocabulary that is often unique to and coined by subgroups, such as teenagers, college students, musicians, skateboarders, computer programmers, street gangs, rap artists, and soldiers. Often used to communicate the unique common experiences of these subgroups, slang is frequently not understood by all segments of society. Most often, slang attempts to be current and trendy, but such language is soon over-used and quickly becomes dated. For instance, in the early part of the twentieth century, the expression *the cat's pyjamas* was the fashionable way to call something or someone excellent; more recently, a *cool dude* might use the slang terms *bad* and *wicked*. Other more current examples of slang include *bummer, grunt, rip-off, wired,* or *preppie*.

Slang can often make story dialogue sound lively and authentic. However, it is inappropriate in formal writing such as academic essays and business letters.

>        failed              examination            has been wasted
> Jeff ~~flunked~~ his final history ~~exam~~, and now his semester ~~is a total write-off~~.

*Slang:* Mel and her gang are coming over and we're going to watch the tube and pig out.

*Formal:* Melanie and her friends are coming over. We are going to watch television and eat snacks.

## REGIONAL EXPRESSIONS

A regional expression is common to a particular area of the country. For instance, in Atlantic Canada, a *barachois* is "a tidal pond partly obstructed by a bar" (*Nelson Canadian Dictionary*).

> Murray could see the skiff beyond the <u>barachois</u>.

Regional expressions, like slang, can add colour and authenticity; however, they may not be familiar to a general audience and should be avoided in formal academic writing.

> *ocean*
> After he caught the winning salmon, they threw the fish into the ~~salt chuck~~.

*Salt chuck* is a regional expression used in British Columbia and the U.S. Pacific Northwest. It might not be known to all Canadians.

Many Canadian dictionaries specify whether a word or expression is regional.

## NON-STANDARD ENGLISH

Non-standard English is acceptable in informal social and regional contexts, but should be avoided in formal writing. Examples of non-standard English include the following words and phrases:

> *ain't, anyways, bursted, hisself, nowheres, theirselves*

Standard English, on the other hand, is the written English commonly expected and used in educational institutions, businesses, government, and other contexts in which people must formally communicate with one another. Use standard English in all of your academic writing. If you are unsure about whether a word or phrase is standard or non-standard English, check a current Canadian dictionary.

> *Non-Standard:* The guy was nowheres in sight, and he could of left town, but she didn't care anyways.

> *Standard:* The man was nowhere in sight. He could have left town, but she did not care anyway.

# LEVELS OF FORMALITY

Informal writing is casual in language and tone. It is appropriate for communication in such forms as notes, friendly letters, e-mails, journal entries, and brief memorandums to people you know well.

Formal writing is formal in tone and language. It is appropriate for academic and business writing, such as essays, research and technical reports, job application letters, and business letters and reports.

When deciding which level of formality to use in your writing, consider two key factors:

1. subject
2. audience

As you draft and revise your work, ask the following questions about the level of formality you select.

## SUBJECT

- Is my choice of words appropriate to the seriousness of my subject?

## AUDIENCE

- What type of language will my audience expect?

- Is my choice of words appropriate for the intended audience?
- Does my choice of words, and the tone these words create, make me seem too close or too distant from my readers?

In academic or business writing, use a formal level of writing and assume a serious tone. The sentence below opens a career application letter too informally.

I'm just dropping you a few lines to put my name in for that fisheries biologist's assistant job I saw somewhere in the *Free Press* a few weeks back.

*More Formal:* I am writing to apply for the position of fisheries biologist's assistant advertised in the June 16 edition of the *Free Press*.

The level of language can also seem too formal.

*Too Formal:* When the illustrious Maple Leafs exited from the frozen playing surface trailing their less renowned opponents, the Wild, by the modest score of 1–0, the assembled spectators vigorously voiced their disapproval. The officials in charge of the National Hockey League were authentic demons for having the audacity to schedule these mismatched contests between the annual All-Star Game and the hockey tournament that is part of Olympic competition.

*More Appropriate:* When the Leafs left the ice trailing the Wild 1–0, loud boos erupted from the crowd. The NHL was the real culprit for scheduling lopsided games like these between the All-Star Game and the Olympics.

## NON-SEXIST LANGUAGE

Sexist language is biased in attributing characteristics and roles to people exclusively on the basis of gender. Sometimes, sexist language is obvious, but often it is less so. Sexist language can be explicit, as in calling an attractive young woman a *hot chick*. It can be patronizing by referring to a mature woman as a *girl Friday*. It can reflect stereotypical thinking by unnecessarily drawing attention to a person's gender, as in a *female university president*. And it can be subtle, yet still highly biased, by including only male pronouns when more inclusive language is needed; for example, *an athlete always needs to maintain his composure*.

Sexist language can apply to men as well as women; for instance, *male kindergarten teacher* draws what may be unnecessary attention to the teacher's gender.

There are several strategies for avoiding sexist language:

1. Treat all people equally in your descriptions of them.

   *Unequal Treatment:* Mr. Delmonico, Mr. Habib, Mr. Dawson, and Tillie, the secretary, arrived for the meeting.

   *Acceptable:* Mr. Delmonico, Mr. Habib, Mr. Dawson, and Ms. Lord arrived for the meeting.

2. Avoid stereotypes.

   *Stereotyping:* Like all men, he hates to cook.

3. Use pairs of pronouns to indicate inclusive gender references.

   *Exclusive:* A professor is motivated by his students.

   *Acceptable:* A professor is motivated by his or her students.

4. Rewrite the sentence as a plural.

   *Acceptable:* Professors are motivated by their students.

5. Rewrite the sentence so there is no gender problem.

   *Acceptable:* A professor is motivated by students.

6. Make gender-neutral word choices.

---

### AVOIDING SEXIST LANGUAGE

| INAPPROPRIATE | GENDER-NEUTRAL |
|---|---|
| alderman | city council member, councillor |
| anchorman | anchor |
| businessman | businessperson, entrepreneur |
| chairman | chairperson, chair |
| clergyman | member of the clergy, minister |
| coed | student |
| craftsman | artisan, craftsperson |
| fireman | firefighter |
| forefather | ancestor |
| foreman | supervisor |
| freshman | first-year student |
| housewife | homemaker |
| mailman | mail carrier, letter carrier, postal worker |
| male nurse | nurse |
| mankind | people, humankind, human |
| manpower | personnel, human resources |
| newsman | journalist, reporter |
| policeman | police officer |
| salesman | salesperson, sales clerk |
| stewardess | flight attendant |
| to man | to staff, to operate |
| weatherman | weather forecaster |
| waitress | server |
| workman | worker, labourer, employee |

---

## CONNOTATIONS

Many words have two levels of meaning: a denotative meaning and a connotative meaning. The denotative meaning of a word is its common, literal, dictionary meaning. The connotative meaning is the word's emotional meaning, which includes experiences and associations you make when you see a word in print or hear it spoken. For example, the dictionary meaning of *eagle* is "a large bird of prey." However, the word *eagle* also carries emotional and associative meanings such as "power," "pride," "majesty," and "fierceness."

When considering any word for a piece of writing, consider both its denotative and connotative meanings. Sometimes, using a word with unknown connotations could imply a meaning you do not intend. Conversely, you can enhance your intended meaning by selecting the word with the most appropriate connotations for your subject, purpose, and audience. Often, reviewing all listed meanings in a dictionary entry will give you a sense of a word's connotations.

laughed
The young women ~~giggled~~ at all the right parts in the comedy.

*Giggled* has an association with immaturity, and because the women were young, the sentence implies that they were immature. The intended meaning of the sentence was that the women appreciated the humour of the play, so *laughed* is more appropriate.

has                                           had

Ethel ~~is a victim of~~ rheumatoid arthritis and has ~~suffered from~~ it for 10 years.

This sentence is even better than the revision marked above: *Ethel was diagnosed with rheumatoid arthritis 10 years ago.* Other emotional language related to suffering is best avoided: this kind of language adds an inappropriate slant to the meaning.

# NOUNS

There are many types of nouns.

## GENERAL AND SPECIFIC NOUNS

Nouns can be general or specific. Suppose a friend asks, "What did you do between classes?" You respond, "I listened to the radio." *Radio* is a broad, general noun. Your response could refer to operating a ham radio transceiver, listening to music over speakers in the student cafeteria, or downloading a broadcast on Internet radio to your laptop. All of these individual alternatives within the general category *radio* are specific nouns.

## ABSTRACT AND CONCRETE NOUNS

Nouns can be abstract or concrete. Abstract nouns refer to concepts, ideas, qualities, and conditions. They are not concrete, for instance, *love, charity, kindness, humanism, youth,* and *integrity.* Concrete nouns name things that are detectable by your senses, for instance, *snake, dill, sunset, coffee, caramel,* and *harp.*

Professional writers spend time selecting the most appropriate and precise word to communicate an idea or feeling. Similarly, in your own writing, try to select the most effective word for your purpose. In your writing projects, you will frequently need to describe, explain, and evaluate general and abstract content. At these times, general and abstract language will be most appropriate. But wherever possible, use specific and concrete nouns to make your writing clear and evocative.

*Toronto's smog*             *launched the sailboat into Lake Ontario*

~~Hazy city air~~ made it difficult to breathe as we ~~put the boat in the water~~.

General abstract nouns, such as *things, considerations,* and *aspects,* are extremely vague and lacking in the precision required by technical communication.

             *shockproof*   *foam EDM and Total Station*

For transport, use ∧ packaging ∧ for the ~~instruments~~.

         *about 8500*         *2.5 million hectares,*

On average, ~~a lot of~~ forest fires, burning ~~large areas,~~ are reported each year in Canada.

# ACTIVE VERBS

Where possible, choose precise verbs that give your writing impact and power.

## WHICH VERBS ARE WEAK?

Weak verbs are forms of the verb *to be* (*be, am, is, are, was, were, being, been*). None of these verb forms communicates a specific action. Verbs in the passive voice—the *be* verb is required to make a passive—tend to lack power. Combine the two—the *be* verb and the passive voice—and you have lifeless writing that fails to communicate: *An acceptable job was done by her.*

## HOW CAN I USE VERBS TO MAKE MY WRITING LIVELY?
Choose precise, vigorous, emphatic, expressive, or descriptive verbs in the active voice. The following sentences show a transition from using a form of the *be* verb and the passive voice to using a precise verb in the active voice.

> *Using Be Verb:* Frequently dynamite *was found useful*, called "shot firing" in Newfoundland, but caused water wells to collapse.

> *Passive Voice:* Frequently water wells *were caused* to collapse by the use of dynamite, called "shot firing" in Newfoundland.

> *Active Voice:* Frequently the use of dynamite, called "shot firing" in Newfoundland, *caused* water wells to collapse.

## WHEN SHOULD I REPLACE THE *BE* VERB?
Change the *be* verb form when it creates a wordy construction. Look for a word that could be turned into a verb in the phrase following the *be* verb.

> to keep
> It is critical ~~that~~ warning labels on equipment ~~be kept~~ clean and legible.

## WHEN SHOULD I NOT REPLACE THE *BE* VERB?

1. You should keep forms of *be* (*be, am, is, are, was, were, being, been*) when you want to link the subject of a sentence with a noun that renames the subject or an adjective that describes it.

   Well logging *is* a technique for recording rock and fluid properties to find hydrocarbon zones below Earth's crust.

2. Keep *be* verb forms when they function as helping verbs before present participles.

   The populations of reintroduced elk in Ontario *are* growing gradually.

3. The *be* verb forms are acceptable when expressing ongoing action.

   At the bridge site, the company was expecting consistent, reliable output of concrete from the mixers to the pier forms.

## WHEN SHOULD I REPLACE A PASSIVE VERB?
With sentences in the active voice, the subject performs the action.

> *Active Voice:* The operator constantly *monitors* the cable tension and depth.
> With sentences in the passive voice, the subject receives the action.

> *Passive Voice:* The cable tension and depth *are* constantly *monitored* by the operator.
> In some passive sentences the performer of the action is not mentioned.

> The cable tension and depth are constantly monitored.

Strong writing clearly states who or what performs actions. Use the active voice by making the person or thing that performs the action the subject of the sentence.

> The steepness of the terrain and the clarity of the image dictate the
> ~~The~~ distance from level to staff ~~is dictated by the steepness of the terrain and the clarity of the image.~~

Use the passive voice in the following writing situations:

1. You want to emphasize who or what receives the action.
2. You want to give less emphasis to the person or thing that performs the action.
3. The person or thing that performs the action is unknown.

For example, in the previous example involving the operator and the cable, you would select the active voice if you wished to emphasize the operator's importance. If you wanted to emphasize the importance of monitoring the cable, you would use the passive voice. And if monitoring the cable was of central importance and the operator of no importance, or if you didn't know who did the monitoring, you would use something like this: *The cable tension and depth are constantly monitored.*

## MISUSED WORDS

When working on a draft, you may want to use a word, but may be unsure of the word's meaning or spelling. Always check the meanings of such words in a reliable dictionary. Misusing words can obscure your overall meaning and create unintentional humour.

site

The engineer on the job ~~sight~~ was looking through the eyepiece of the dumpy level.

## STANDARD IDIOMS

An idiom is an expression whose meaning cannot be determined simply by knowing the definition of each word within the idiom. Many idioms are colourful and easy to spot: *kill two birds with one stone, read between the lines, the last straw.*

An idiom always appears in one particular form, one that may not necessarily be taken literally. An example of an idiom is *beside oneself. She was beside herself* means "She was in a state of extreme excitement or agitation."

Using idiomatic expressions with prepositions can be tricky. An unidiomatic expression may make better literal sense, but the idiomatic expression is used because it is accepted English usage. If you are in doubt, check a good Canadian dictionary by looking up the word before the preposition.

| UNIDIOMATIC | IDIOMATIC |
|---|---|
| according with | according to |
| angry at | angry with |
| capable to | capable of |
| comply to | comply with |
| desirous to | desirous of |
| different than | different from |
| go by | go to |
| intend on doing | intend to do |
| off of | off |
| plan on doing | plan to do |
| preferable than | preferable to |
| prior than | prior to |
| recommend her to do | recommend that she do |
| superior than | superior to |
| sure and | sure to |
| try and | try to |
| type of a | type of |
| wait on a person | wait for a person |
| wait on line | wait in line |
| with reference in | with reference to |

## CLICHÉS

A cliché is a phrase or expression that has become tired and predictable due to over-use; hence, writing with clichés seems stale. Here are some clichés to avoid in your writing:

> add insult to injury, at long last, a word to the wise, cool as a cucumber, cold as ice, easier said than done, few and far between, first and foremost, for all intents and purposes, finishing touches, good as gold, hit the nail on the head, in the long run, it stands to reason, narrow escape, red-letter day, this day and age

You might make a database in a computer file of other clichés to avoid.

Clichés, by being so predictable, deprive writing of any sense of surprise. However, in some rare instances, you might inject freshness into a cliché by giving it an unexpected twist.

> Suitable sites for the new project are *few and far between*; the surveyors logged more than 200 km between potential locations.

PUNCTUATION

Punctuation is an essential part of clear, grammatical writing. It makes your sentences logical and readable, and provides a signal to the reader of how something is to be understood. Without it, most readers and writers would be hopelessly lost. Although the rules for correct punctuation are quite detailed, they are basically straightforward. This section will help you to master proper punctuation; practice will make it second nature.

## ▮ THE COMMA

Frequently, a comma is essential to ensure that readers clearly understand your intended meaning. Omitting or misplacing commas can easily lead to misreadings.

> The staff says the boss is lazy.
>
> The staff, says the boss, is lazy.

### INDEPENDENT CLAUSES WITH COORDINATING CONJUNCTION

In some sentences, two or more independent clauses (clauses that can stand on their own as sentences) are linked by coordinating conjunctions (*and, or, for, but, so, nor,* and *yet*). In such sentences, place a comma before the coordinating conjunction.

> A dried sample of soil is shaken through a vertical stack of sieves, and a lab assistant records the mass retained on each sieve.

*Exception:* If the two independent clauses are short, and there is no chance of misinterpreting the sentence, the comma may be omitted.

> The Greyhound bus pulled in and we boarded it.

# INTRODUCTORY ELEMENTS

## COMMAS WITH INTRODUCTORY CLAUSES

An introductory adverbial clause is a construction with a subject and a verb that introduces a main clause.

When the combination of weather and fuel moisture reach extreme hazard levels

ᐱ a ban on campfires, on camping, and on working in the forest will be put in place to try to prevent forest fires.

If the time between first and last transmission path exceeds the time between transmitted symbols

ᐱ intersymbol interference (ISI) occurs.

If the phrase or clause is brief, and there is no danger of misreading the sentence, the comma may be omitted.

In a flash it was over.

## COMMAS WITH LONGER INTRODUCTORY PHRASES

After longer introductory phrases, use a comma to indicate that the main part of the sentence is about to start.

In addition to sensor-based measurements on the surface

ᐱ robotic equipment can sample formation fluids in the borehole. (prepositional phrase)

Verbal phrases include participles, gerunds, and infinitives.

Combined with high winds and lightning strikes in remote areas

ᐱ dry conditions can result in fire activity that cannot be stopped using current firefighting resources and technology. (verbal phrase)

In moving energy through food webs ᐱ benthic macroinvertebrates are important. (verbal phrase)

To isolate any local movements ᐱ place at least three permanent benchmarks. (infinitive phrase)

Follow an introductory absolute phrase with a comma.

All theoretical issues considered ᐱ LIDAR systems seem to have been invented by different manufacturers in different ways using different technologies.

# ITEMS IN A SERIES

A series in a sentence could be three or more words, phrases, or clauses that have the same grammatical form and are of equal importance. Place a comma after each item in the series. An item might be one word, a phrase, or a clause.

The under-slab inspection of the site is performed after the base course is prepared, the vapour barrier is in place, and reinforcing materials are positioned.

# COORDINATE ADJECTIVES

Coordinate adjectives are two or more adjectives that separately and equally modify the noun or pronoun. The order of these adjectives can be changed without affecting the meaning of the sentence. Coordinate adjectives can be joined by *and*. Separate coordinate adjectives with commas.

> The <u>small, shallow, fast-flowing</u> mountain streams differed in a number of physicochemical variables.

# CUMULATIVE ADJECTIVES

Cumulative adjectives modify the adjective after them and a noun or pronoun. Cumulative adjectives increase meaning from word to word as they progress toward the noun or pronoun. They are not interchangeable and cannot be joined by *and*.

*Do not use a comma between cumulative adjectives.*

> The book talk featured <u>three well-known English</u> authors.

> His resumé included <u>various short-term landscaping</u> jobs.

> An exhibit of <u>authentic early Inca</u> art was on display at the Royal Ontario Museum.

> The music festival featured many <u>Canadian folk</u> acts.

# RESTRICTIVE AND NON-RESTRICTIVE ELEMENTS

Adjective clauses, adjective phrases, and appositives can modify nouns and pronouns. These modifying elements may be either restrictive or non-restrictive.

### WHAT IS A RESTRICTIVE ELEMENT?

A restrictive element limits, defines, or identifies the noun or pronoun that it modifies. The information in a restrictive element is essential to a sentence's meaning. *Do not set off a restrictive element with commas.*

> Stream water <u>that contained naturally drifting invertebrates</u> was fed through black polyethylene pipes into a header tank.

### WHAT IS A NON-RESTRICTIVE ELEMENT?

A non-restrictive element adds non-essential, or parenthetical, information about an idea or term that is already limited, defined, or identified; hence, a non-restrictive element is set off with commas or a single comma if the element ends the sentence.

> This bubble, <u>which then provides a horizontal line of sight in the direction of the collimation axis</u>, can be levelled with the instrument's footscrews.

In some cases, however, you will need to know the context in which a sentence appears in order to decide whether a restrictive or non-restrictive element is required.

> This bubble that is levelled with the instrument's footscrews provides a horizontal line of sight in the direction of the collimation axis.

## CONCLUDING ADVERB CLAUSES

Adverb clauses introducing a sentence almost always conclude with a comma. However, when adverb clauses conclude a sentence and their meaning is essential to the sentence, they are not set off with commas. Adverb clauses that begin with the following subordinated conjunctions are usually essential:

*after, as soon as, before, because, if, since, unless, until, when*

Water boils at sea level ˏwhen it reaches a temperature of 100°C.

Place a comma before adverb clauses that contain non-essential information. Often, adverb clauses beginning with the following subordinating conjunctions are non-essential:

*although, even though, though, whereas*

The timber quota holder must submit annual operating and general development plans, although the province is responsible for overall forest planning in the area.

## TRANSITIONS, PARENTHETICAL EXPRESSIONS, ABSOLUTE PHRASES, CONTRASTS

### TRANSITIONAL EXPRESSIONS

Transitional expressions are words or groups of words that function as links between or within sentences. A transitional expression can appear at the beginning or end of a sentence or within it. Examples of transitional expressions are conjunctive adverbs, such as *therefore* and *however*, and transitional phrases, such as *for example, in addition*, and *on the contrary*.

If a transitional expression appears between independent clauses in a compound sentence, place a semicolon before it and, most often, a comma after the transitional expression.

Biological communities at undisturbed sites will be broadly similar; therefore, the range of benthic organisms constitutes a type-specific biological target.

The problem of poorly selected study subjects is particularly acute when response rates are low; for example, a key question is the demographic profile of website users.

Set off a transitional expression with commas if it appears at the beginning of a sentence or in the middle of an independent clause.

As a result ˏfire and fire suppression change an ecosystem considered from environmental, economic, and social viewpoints.

Set up a shelter with a heater; this shelter must not ˏhowever ˏobstruct your view of the well-head assembly.

In some cases, if the transitional expression is integrated with the sentence and requires no more than a minimal pause when being read, no commas are needed to set off the expression. Expressions such as the following do not always have to be set off with commas:

*at least, certainly, consequently, indeed, of course, perhaps, then, therefore, undoubtedly*

The earth's equator may be an ellipse rather than a circle; <u>therefore</u> the ellipsoid is triaxial.

All plant maintenance schedules must be strictly followed and proper documentation maintained; documenting will confirm that <u>indeed</u> such servicing and repairs have been made.

## PARENTHETICAL EXPRESSIONS

Parenthetical expressions contain additional information that the writer inserts into the sentence to explain, qualify, or give a point of view. If parenthetical expressions do not appear in parentheses, they are set off with commas.

High-pressure water, up to 2000 psi, is used in hydraulic well stimulation.

While commas are required to set off distinctly parenthetical expressions, do *not* use commas to set off mildly parenthetical expressions.

After setup, the laser unit itself, finally, sends out a series of light pulses.

## ABSOLUTE PHRASES

An absolute phrase contains a noun subject and a participle that modify an entire sentence. Set off absolute phrases with commas.

<u>A graduated staff being held vertically over the first point</u>, read the intersection of the cross-hair with the image of the staff.

<u>The dried sample now placed on the top sieve</u>, put the sieves in the mechanical shaker and shake for seven minutes.

## EXPRESSIONS OF CONTRAST

Expressions of contrast include words such as *not, nor, but,* or *unlike.* Set off expressions of contrast with commas.

A preservative of 70% ethanol in water, <u>unlike formalin</u>, does not fix tissues of crustaceans and insects.

The meter's oscillations will slow when the flow in the river current slows, <u>but continue as long as the river water is moving rapidly around the rock.</u>

## NOUNS OF DIRECT ADDRESS, *YES* AND *NO*, INTERROGATIVE TAGS, INTERJECTIONS

Use commas to set off the following:

- nouns of direct address

  Your back flip, <u>Olga</u>, is of Olympic calibre.

- the words *yes* and *no*

  <u>No</u>, you cannot rappel down the face of the university administration tower.

- interrogative tags

  You did turn off the iron, <u>didn't you</u>?

- mild interjections

  <u>Then</u>, incidents like that are inevitable.

## *HE SAID,* ETC.

Use commas with speech tags, such as *she said* or *he said*, to set off direct quotations.

Sir Sandford Fleming wrote, "Divisions of time, like links in an unbroken chain, follow one another consecutively; they have no separate contemporaneous existence; they continue portions of the same time."

"I am a great believer in luck, and I find the harder I work the more I have of it," said Stephen Leacock.

## DATES, ADDRESSES, TITLES, NUMBERS

### DATES

When the date is shown in month-day-year style within the sentence, put commas after the day numeral and the year.

On August 14, 1945, Japan surrendered.

When the date is inverted or when only the month and year are given, commas are not required.

The birthday is celebrated on 24 May 2006.

January 2006 was unseasonably warm.

### ADDRESSES

Use a comma between the names of the city and province/territory or city and country. When a sentence continues on after the city and province or city and country are identified, put a comma after the name of the province or country, as well.

Stephen Leacock died in Toronto, Ontario, in 1944.

In a complete address, insert commas to separate all items except the postal code.

I would appreciate it if you would courier the book to Ennis James at 126 Mayfield Drive, Oakville, Ontario L6H 1K7.

### TITLES

When an abbreviated title follows a name, place a comma after the name and a second comma after the title.

Philip Bacho, Ph.D., taught the course on writing scripts.

### NUMBERS

Canada follows the international system of metric measurement, which does not use commas in numbers. Instead, spaces are used to separate sets of three digits. Four-digit numbers may be grouped together.

In your reading, you may encounter commas used after every three digits to the right for numbers that are four digits or more. This system was used before Canada adopted the international metric system.

4673          233 971          6 299 381

Never use commas to separate sets of digits in years, telephone numbers, street numbers, or postal codes.

## TO PREVENT CONFUSION

In many writing situations, commas are required to prevent reader confusion.

### ECHOING WORDS

When two words repeat or strongly echo each other, a comma helps to clarify sentence meaning.

Asked about safety on the fire line, he said he felt that whatever <u>happens</u>,<u>happens</u>.

### CLARIFYING A WRITER'S INTENTION

Occasionally, commas are required to help readers group units of meaning as the writer intended.

<u>Those who can</u>, run every chance they get.

## ■ THE SEMICOLON

A semicolon is used to separate major elements of a sentence that are of equal grammatical rank.

## INDEPENDENT CLAUSES WITH NO COORDINATING CONJUNCTION

An independent clause expresses a complete thought and can stand on its own as a sentence. When related independent clauses appear together in a sentence—a compound sentence—they are usually linked by a comma and a coordinating conjunction (*and, but, for, nor, or, so,* and *yet*). The conjunction indicates the relationship between the clauses.

When the relationship between independent clauses is clear without the conjunction, you may instead link the two clauses with a semicolon.

Attach the split-barrel sampler to the A-rod; lower it into the hole until it is sitting on the undisturbed material.

Use a semicolon if a coordinating conjunction between two independent clauses has been omitted. If you use a comma, you will create a grammatical error known as a comma splice.

It has a vertical laser plumb; the unit can be used for both horizontal and vertical applications in self-levelling mode.

Strategies for revising comma splice errors can be found on pages 67 to 69. You may wish to consider other alternatives to using a semicolon.

## INDEPENDENT CLAUSES WITH TRANSITIONAL EXPRESSIONS

Transitional expressions can be conjunctive adverbs or transitional phrases.

*Common Conjunctive Adverbs*
*accordingly, also, anyway, besides, certainly, consequently, conversely, finally, further, furthermore, hence, however, incidentally, indeed, instead, likewise, meanwhile, moreover, namely, nevertheless, next, nonetheless, now, otherwise, similarly, specifically, still, subsequently, then, thereafter, therefore, thus, undoubtedly*

*Transitional Phrases*
*after all, as a matter of fact, as an illustration, as a result, at any rate, at the same time, equally important, even so, for example, for instance, in addition, in conclusion, in fact, in other words, in short, in spite of, in summary, in the first place, in the same way, of course, on the contrary, on the other hand, to be sure, to illustrate*

When a transitional expression comes between independent clauses, place a semi-colon before the expression and a comma after it.

She is an authority on the West Nile virus; furthermore, we need someone with her expertise.

If the transitional expression is in the middle of or at the end of the second independent clause, the semicolon is placed between the independent clauses.

Generally, people who work at the biological station have advanced postsecondary degrees; Tony, on the other hand, acquired his knowledge and expertise through practical experience.

Do not confuse the punctuation for transitional expressions with that used with coordinating conjunctions (*and, but, for, nor, or, so,* and *yet*). When a coordinating conjunction links two independent clauses, it is preceded by a comma. (See page 109.)

## SERIES WITH INTERNAL PUNCTUATION

Usually, commas separate items in a series. However, when series items contain commas, a semicolon is placed between items to make the sentence easier to read.

The inspection team consisted of R.L. Chapman, project engineer; J.L. Jones, supervising technologist; and W.H. Heinrich, consulting architect.

## INCORRECT USES OF THE SEMICOLON

Never use a semicolon in the following writing situations:

- between independent clauses joined by *and, but, for, nor, or, so,* or *yet*

  *runway, and*
  Turning around outside of the buttons causes rutting on the ~~runway; and~~ the damages are incurred by the department.

- between a subordinate clause and the remainder of the sentence

  *falls, seeding*
  Because the drilling was completed after significant snow ~~falls; seeding~~ was not carried out.

- between an appositive and the word to which it refers

  *overburden, principally*
  Index tests gave a preliminary classification of the ~~overburden; principally~~ Pleistocene materials.

- to introduce a list

  *areas: measuring*
  The project covers three research ~~areas; measuring~~ forest structure, mapping forest topography, and simulating space-borne LIDAR data from airborne LIDAR.

# ▊ THE COLON

The colon is used most often to indicate a formal, emphatic introductory word, phrase, or clause that follows it.

## BEFORE A LIST, AN APPOSITIVE, A QUOTATION

Use a colon before

- a list

  For this experiment, you will need the following materials: <u>three clear, colourless liquids in numbered cups; a transparent sheet; a waterproof marker; an eyedropper or a small measuring spoon; and paper towels.</u>

- an appositive

  The photos undergo a correction process to compensate for distortions caused by terrain relief, lens distortion, earth curvature, and changes caused by minor variations in the flight platform: <u>the ortho rectification process.</u>

- a quotation

  Frederick Banting summed up his view of innovation this way: "<u>No one has ever had an idea in a dress suit.</u>"

  For additional ways of introducing quotations, see pages 122 to 123.

## BETWEEN INDEPENDENT CLAUSES

To erect the piers, crews use a slip form system: they pour 400 cubic yards of concrete at a time, they reconfigure the forms, and they repeat the process twice more.

You can use a capital letter or a lowercase letter to begin the independent clause after the colon.

## CONVENTIONAL USES

The colon is conventionally used

- after the salutation of a formal letter

  Dear Ms. Pointman:

- to indicate hours and minutes

  6:31 a.m. (or A.M.)

- between numbers in ratios

  Mix dry materials with a water-to-cement ratio of no more than 1:1.8 to make concrete.

- between the title and subtitle of a book or journal article

  Incorporation of nitrogen and carbon from spawning coho salmon into the trophic system of small streams: evidence from stable isotopes

- to separate the city from the publisher and date in a bibliographic entry

  Toronto: Nelson, 2009.

- between Bible chapters and verses

  Psalms 23:1–3

## INCORRECT USES OF THE COLON

Except in documentation, a complete independent clause must precede a colon.

*Do not use a colon in the following writing situations:*

- between a verb and its complement or object

  An important relationship in soil engineering is ꝏunconfined compressive strength equal to twice the cohesion or shear strength of a clay soil.

- between a preposition and its object

  Soils may be classified into ꝏfine grained or coarse grained.

- after for *example, such as,* and *including/included*

  The content of the botanist's lecture included ꝏ boreal forests, a Carolinian forest, and an Amazonian rain forest.

## ▌THE APOSTROPHE

## POSSESSIVE NOUNS

An apostrophe (') appears as part of a noun to indicate that the word is possessive. Often, ownership is obvious, as in *Mishka's hockey stick* or *the instructor's briefcase*. Sometimes ownership is not as explicit, as in *the journey's end* or *the river's tributaries*. To determine whether a noun is possessive, see if you can state it as an *of* phrase, as in *the end of the journey* or *the tributaries of the river*. In these examples, both nouns—*journey's* and *river's*— are possessive.

### ADD -'S IF

1. The noun does not end in -s.

   Pressure pulses transmit data to the surface in the <u>well's</u> mud fluid column.

   Biological controls are sometimes used to disrupt the target <u>insect's</u> life cycle.

2. The noun is singular and ends in -s.

   <u>Gus's</u> father owns a single-engine plane.

### ADD ONLY AN APOSTROPHE IF

The noun is plural and ends in -s

   <u>Workers'</u> rights were neglected by the military regime.

### WITH COMPOUND SUBJECTS

With a compound subject, use -'s (or -s') with the last noun only to show joint possession.

   You should see Doug and <u>Dino's</u> modified stock car.

   Make all nouns possessive to show individual possession.

   <u>Todd's</u> and <u>Margaret's</u> ideas on how to decorate the home were diametrically opposed.

### WITH COMPOUND NOUNS

Use -'s (or -s') with the last element in a compound noun to show possession.

   My sister-in-<u>law's</u> film won a Genie.

## POSSESSIVE INDEFINITE PRONOUNS

An indefinite pronoun refers to a general or non-specific person or thing. Examples of indefinite pronouns are *somebody*, *anything*, and *anyone*. Add -'s to the end of the indefinite pronoun to make it possessive.

It is not <u>anybody's</u> business what I do in my free time.

<u>Someone's</u> laptop was stolen from the reference library.

## CONTRACTIONS

The apostrophe takes the place of missing letters in contractions.

<u>Who's</u> going to do it <u>doesn't</u> matter.

The apostrophe can also indicate that the first two digits of years have been left out.

There will be a reunion for the class of '<u>88</u>.

Did you enjoy *That '<u>70s</u> Show?*

However, -s without an apostrophe is added to years in a decade.

She lived in Paris in the <u>1940s</u>.

## PLURALS OF NUMBERS, LETTERS, ETC.

Other common writing situations where -'s is used to pluralize include

- lower case letters

  The DNA chains formed a series of  *<u>s's</u>*.

- words as words

  I don't want to have to deal with any more  *<u>what if's</u>*

Notice that -s is not italicized when used with italicized words or letters.

No apostrophe is needed with plurals of numbers, upper case letters, and abbreviations.

He has trouble writing <u>6s</u>.

I bought some new <u>DVDs</u>.

The ends of the channel pipes should look like a row of <u>Ls</u> against the top plate.

## INCORRECT USES OF THE APOSTROPHE

*Do not use an apostrophe with*

- nouns that are not possessive

  The clients' had expected us to pick up the tab for dinner.

- the possessive pronouns *his*, *hers*, *its*, *ours*, *theirs*, and *whose*

  A fibreglass screen below the specimen facilitated it's removal for dry mass determinations.

Here, *its* is the possessive form. *It's* is the contraction for *it is*.

## DIRECT QUOTATIONS

Direct quotations are the exact words copied from a print source or transcribed from what a person says. Direct quotations must be enclosed within quotation marks.

> "<u>The open ocean is normally a friendly environment for a sea kayak</u>," writes John Dowd in *Sea Kayaking: A Manual for Long-Distance Touring*.

On the other hand, indirect quotations paraphrase or summarize what has appeared in a print source or what a person has said. Indirect quotations are not placed within quotation marks.

> John Dowd professes that generally the open ocean is a safe place to sea kayak.

### QUOTING LONGER PASSAGES BY A SINGLE SPEAKER

If you are directly quoting passages by a single speaker, start each new paragraph with quotation marks, but do not use closing quotation marks until the end of the quoted material.

## LONG QUOTATIONS

### PROSE

A "long" quotation of prose is any passage that is more than four typed or handwritten lines. Indent the entire quotation 10 spaces from the left margin. You do not need to enclose the longer quotation within quotation marks because the indented format establishes for the reader that the quotation is taken exactly from a source. Usually, longer quotations are introduced by a sentence ending with a colon.

> Smoking can destroy the health of smokers and is a very real health risk to those around them, as Clark (2009: 161) points out:
>
> > In 1995, 4.5 million nonsmoking Canadians aged 15 and over were exposed to cigarette smoke on a daily basis. Another 2.2 million were exposed to it at least once a week, while about 840 000 were exposed to it less frequently. In terms of percentages, about 28 percent of nonsmokers aged 15 and over breathed secondhand smoke every day, while about 19 percent were exposed to it somewhat less often. Just over half of nonsmokers reported that they were not exposed to ETS (environmental tobacco smoke).

Placing the page number within parentheses follows the name-year citation style prescribed by the Council of Science Editors (see Chapter 10).

If the direct quotation had included additional paragraphs, the first line of each new paragraph would need to be indented an additional three spaces.

## QUOTATIONS WITHIN QUOTATIONS

Single quotation marks enclose quotations within quotations.

> According to Newman et al., Charles de Gaulle "<u>spoke the words that jolted a nation: 'Vive le Québec libre!'</u> "

Two different quotation marks appear at the end of the quotation. The single quotation mark completes the interior quotation, while the double quotation mark completes the main quotation.

# TITLES

Use quotation marks around titles of works that are included within other works, such as newspaper and journal articles, radio programs, television documentaries, and chapters and other subdivisions of books.

> His talk focused on the limnology of freshwater streams, as discussed in Chapter 5, "Habitat, Life History, and Behavioral Adaptations of Aquatic Insects," of Merritt and Cummins' *An Introduction to the Aquatic Insects of North America*.

The titles of books and journals appear in italics.

# WORDS AS WORDS

Italics or underlining is preferred for setting off words used as words. However, it is acceptable to use quotation marks for this purpose.

> The term *environmental assessment* refers to a systematic planning process that guides decisions in support of environmentally sound economic development.

> The term "environmental assessment" refers to a systematic planning process that guides decisions in support of environmentally sound economic development.

# WITH OTHER PUNCTUATION

The following section provides rules for using punctuation with quotation marks.

## COMMAS AND PERIODS

Place commas and periods inside quotation marks.

> "I'm not finished yet," she said. "The books I looked at were of no help."

Also follow the above punctuation rule in the following cases:

1. with single quotation marks
2. for titles of works
3. for words used as words

## SEMICOLONS AND COLONS

Place semicolons and colons outside quotation marks.

> He explained his term "cadastral": a legal boundary survey.

> Bentonite clay is pumped into the annular space through a "tremie tube"; most drillers use a 1 to 1½-inch diameter pipe for this purpose.

## QUESTION MARKS AND EXCLAMATION POINTS

If the question mark or exclamation point is part of the quoted material, place the question mark or exclamation point inside the quotation marks.

> *Part of the Quoted Material*
> When Jeff heard what Susan had done, he shouted, "She made the shot from centre court!"

If the question mark or exclamation point applies to the entire sentence, place the question mark or exclamation point outside the quotation marks.

> *Applies to the Entire Sentence*
> What do you think of Napoleon's view that "history is a set of lies agreed upon"?

# INTRODUCING QUOTED MATERIAL

You have three main punctuation options when using a group of words to introduce a quotation:

1. a colon
2. a comma
3. no punctuation

## WHEN TO USE THE COLON

Use the colon if the quotation has been formally introduced. A formal introduction is a complete independent clause.

> In *The Globe and Mail,* John Stackhouse presents the following insight about political change in Africa: "The economic revolution that has swept through Africa, from the highlands of eastern Kenya to the rain forests of Ivory Coast, has affected almost every African—and altered few governments."

## WHEN TO USE THE COMMA

Use a comma if a quotation is introduced with or followed by an expression such as *she said* or *he uttered.*

> Giving fresh meaning to a cliché, the smoke jumper said, "Where there's smoke, there's fire."

> "I'm a Canadian," I protested.

## WHEN A QUOTATION IS BLENDED INTO A SENTENCE

Use a comma or no punctuation, depending on how the quotation fits into the grammatical structure of the sentence.

> She walked with an awkward jerky gait, as though she were not at home on her own legs, and as she passed by, the other kids would whisper, "Pigeon-Toed Cochran!"

> In summertime, all expeditions were planned tentatively; sentences ended with the phrase "if it doesn't rain."

## WHEN A QUOTATION BEGINS A SENTENCE

Use a comma to set off a quotation at the beginning of a sentence.

> "I'll be back in a moment," I told my students, and half out of my mind with anxiety, I went down in the elevator, dashed across the street, and burst into Adriana's house.

However, a comma is not needed if the opening quotation ends with a question mark or an exclamation point.

> "What are you doing?" I demanded.

## WHEN A QUOTED SENTENCE IS INTERRUPTED BY EXPLANATORY WORDS

Use commas to set off the explanatory words.

> "No," he called back, "I can see it breathing!"

## WHEN TWO SUCCESSIVE QUOTED SENTENCES ARE INTERRUPTED BY EXPLANATORY WORDS

Use a comma before the explanatory words within the quotation marks of the first quotation. End the explanatory words with a period.

> "We are simply not well prepared for the rapid development that we have been experiencing," Dr. Muangman said. "Politicians and decision makers think that if we make a lot of money, that is enough."

## INCORRECT USES OF QUOTATION MARKS

*Do not use quotation marks around indirect quotations.*

> My mother always said longingly that she'd "like to visit Greece."

*Do not use quotation marks to call attention to a word or expression.* Never use quotation marks to distance yourself from an expression or to call attention to slang.

> Some might say the mechanic went on a "busman's holiday."

Do not use quotation marks to set off the title of your own essay, report, or document.

# OTHER MARKS

## PERIOD

Periods are commonly used to indicate the end of a sentence and abbreviations within it.

### ENDING SENTENCES

Use periods after statements, indirect questions, and mild commands.

#### STATEMENT

Use a period after a statement.

> Rock climbing on the Bruce Trail can be dangerous.

#### INDIRECT QUESTION

After a direct question, use a question mark.

> Do you want to walk the Gun Point Loop section of the trail?

However, if the question is indirect, use a period to end the sentence.

> The hike leader inquired if they wanted to walk the Gun Point Loop section of the trail.

#### MILD COMMAND

After a mild command—an imperative or declarative sentence that is not an exclamation—use a period.

> Please pick up the groceries.

However, after a strong command, use the exclamation point.

> Call an ambulance!

## ABBREVIATIONS

Use periods in abbreviations such as the following:

| | | | | |
|---|---|---|---|---|
| a.m. (or A.M.) | p. | B.A. | Dr. | Inc. |
| p.m. (or P.M.) | etc. | M.A. | Ms. | Ltd. |
| B.C. (or B.C.E.) | e.g. | M.B.A. | Mrs. | Dec. |
| A.D. (or C.E.) | i.e. | Ph.D. | Mr. | St. |

*Do not use periods with Canada Post abbreviations*, such as SK, ON, and NB.

Widely recognized abbreviations for organizations, companies, and countries do not require periods, although periods are often used in *U.K.* and *U.S.*

CBC   CSIS   NFB   UK   US   IBM   UN   NBA   CFL

Most abbreviations for technical units of measurement are written without periods.

rpm   ha   psi   Btu   µg/l

If you are in doubt about whether an abbreviation requires a period, check in a current Canadian dictionary or dictionary of technical terms. To check the abbreviation of a company's name, consult that company's website.

*Do not add a second period if the sentence ends with an abbreviation's period.*

He always wanted to complete his M.Sc.

# QUESTION MARK

### FOLLOWING A DIRECT QUESTION

Use a question mark after any direct questions.

How do clay-size particles have major influence on engineering properties?

Use a question mark after a polite request.

Would you please forward to me a copy of the article for my files?

Use a period after an indirect question.

Selby asked if she could go home.

### FOLLOWING QUESTIONS IN A SERIES THAT ARE NOT COMPLETE SENTENCES

Use a question mark to end each question in a series, even if series questions are not complete sentences.

We are curious to hear what Justin's career goal will be this week. Maybe a brain surgeon? Perhaps a stockbroker? Or maybe a travel agent?

# EXCLAMATION POINT

Use the exclamation point with an emphatic declaration or a strong command.

The plane will hit the mountain!

Get out of the way, quickly!

*Do not over-use the exclamation point.*

> *Over-use:* We climbed the mountain on Hornby and had an incredible view! On one side was the snowcapped Coastal Range! On the other side, we could see majestic Mount Washington!

> *Correction:* We climbed the mountain on Hornby and had an incredible view. On one side was the snowcapped Coastal Range. On the other side, we could see majestic Mount Washington.

# DASH

The dash marks a strong break in the continuity of a sentence. It can be used to add information, emphasize part of a sentence, or set off part of the sentence for clarity.

To make a dash on a computer, enter two hyphens without space before the first or after the second. Many computer programs automatically format dashes when you enter two consecutive hyphens. Another option is to use the "Insert Symbol" feature in your software.

Use dashes to

- enclose a sentence element that interrupts the flow of thought, or to set off parenthetical material that deserves emphasis

  Place the zero-depth point on the probe level with the casing top—the top of the Gerhart-Owen cable head is used as the zero-depth position—and zero the depth at the data acquisition system.

- set off appositives that contain commas

  Silviculture—the practice of establishing, tending, and reproducing stands of trees—is one of the most important disciplines in the science of forestry.

- show a dramatic shift in tone or thought

  The cougar, the second largest cat with the broadest range of all terrestrial mammals in the Americas, is extremely elusive and a master of camouflage—and can launch a lightning-fast charge.

- restate

  The ellipsoid of revolution—the figure that would be obtained by rotating an ellipse about its shorter axis—is the geometrical figure used to most nearly approximate the shape of the earth.

- amplify

  Good quality concrete for severe applications has the correct concrete mix design—strong, dense, water-tight, resistant to freeze-thaw action.

- prepare a list

  Add a label to the inside of the specimen jar accurately describing the sample data—the sampling location (stream name and site number), date, name of the collector, and a duplicate label.

*Do not over-use dashes.* If over-used, dashes can lose their effectiveness and make writing disjointed. It is better to limit the number of dashes in a sentence to two paired dashes or one unpaired dash.

*Over-use:* Three students—Anwar, Sanjah, and Pete—won prizes—scholarships, books, and medallions. This is quite an achievement—especially for Pete since he studies only minimally—if at all.

*Correction:* Three students—Anwar, Sanjah, and Pete—won prizes, which included scholarships, books, and medallions. This is quite an achievement, especially for Pete, since he studies only minimally, if at all.

## PARENTHESES

Parentheses are used to set off helpful, non-essential, additional information. While dashes usually call attention to the information they enclose, parentheses often de-emphasize the information they enclose.

Use parentheses to

- enclose supplemental information, such as definitions, examples, digressions or asides, and contrasts

  Calgary is fourth among cities in Canada for number of head offices located within its city limits (280 in 2002).

- enclose scientific names of species

  White rot decays the heartwood and is the main limitation to growing trembling aspen *(Populus tremuloides)* or large-tooth aspen *(Populus grandidentata)* older than 50 years.

- enclose letters or numbers that label items in a series

  Fix oxygen in the sample by the following method: (1) remove any air bubbles by shaking the bottle, (2) add 8 drops of manganese sulphate solution and 8 drops of alkaline potassium iodide, (3) shake to mix, and (4) add 8 drops of sulphuric acid.

*Do not over-use parentheses.* Including too much parenthetical information can make your writing seem choppy and awkward. Often you can integrate information from parentheses into your sentences so they will flow smoothly.

  In rotary-drilled wells, the borehole diameter is two to three inches larger ~~(sufficient annular space to grout the well properly)~~ than the diameter of the casing to be installed, thus allowing sufficient annular space to grout the well properly.

## BRACKETS

Brackets are used to enclose any explanatory words you insert into a direct quotation and to indicate an error in the original quoted material.

### TO ADD OR SUBSTITUTE CLARIFYING INFORMATION IN A QUOTATION

  Clearcutting is not "cutting everything [trees] we want."

### TO INDICATE ERRORS IN ORIGINAL MATERIAL

The Latin word *sic* means "so" or "thus." The word *sic* is placed in brackets immediately after a word in a quotation that appears erroneous or odd. *Sic* indicates that the word is quoted exactly as it stands in the original.

  "You should always make sure a qualified engineer has deigned [sic] your footing forms."

# ELLIPSIS MARK

An ellipsis mark consists of three spaced periods (. . .). The ellipsis is used to indicate that you have omitted material from the original writer's quoted words.

## WHEN DELETING MATERIAL FROM A QUOTATION

Gagnon states that "as much as 65% to 70% of semen volume originates from the seminal vesicles . . . and about 5% from the minor sexual glands."

An ellipsis is not required at the beginning of a quotation. Do not place an ellipsis at the end of the quotation unless you have omitted content from the final quoted sentence.

## WHEN DELETING A FULL SENTENCE FROM THE MIDDLE OF A QUOTED PASSAGE

Use a period before the three ellipsis points if you need to delete a full sentence or more from the middle of a quoted passage.

Follett argues that "Technology developers mustn't merely look at their work as a series of interesting puzzles to solve. . . . They need to consider . . . who it is that will one day be buying their product, bringing it into their homes, and living with it every day."

# SLASH

## USING THE SLASH TO INDICATE OPTIONS OR PAIRED ITEMS

Sometimes the slash is used between options or paired items. Examples include actor/producer, life/death, pass/fail. In these cases, do not leave a space before and after the slash.

Since the project was short of funds, he served as chief engineer/project manager.

Avoid the use of *he/she, his/her*, and *and/or* because they are informal and awkward in writing.

# MECHANICS

9

The mechanical details of a document often contribute much to creating a good first impression on your reader. Care and consistency with details will help to ensure your credibility as a writer. Little things mean a lot.

The conventions of technical style have particular significance for the technical writer. Numbers, abbreviations, hyphenation, scientific notation, and mathematical equations are the mechanical forms for the data transmitted in technical communication. Most technical writers are unfamiliar with conventions used in general writing for numbers, abbreviations, and hyphenation. Therefore this chapter will include these conventions, as well as the more specific conventions in technical style.

## ■ CAPITALIZATION

Capitalize the first word of every sentence. You will also need to capitalize specific types of words within sentences. Use the following rules as general guidelines for capitalization. Consult your dictionary to determine which words must be capitalized.

### PROPER VS. COMMON NOUNS

First of all, a noun is a word or even a group of words used to name or identify any of a class of persons, places, or things. There are also proper nouns, or nouns that name or identify particular persons, places, or things. Capitalize proper nouns and words derived from them, but do not capitalize common nouns.

As a general rule, capitalize the names of the following:

- religions, religious practitioners, holy books, special religious days, and deities
- geographic places
- people's names and nicknames

- words of family relationship used as names (e.g., Uncle Bill)
- nationalities, tribes, races, and languages
- historical events, periods, movements, documents, and treaties
- political parties, organizations, and government departments
- educational institutions, departments, degrees, and specific courses
- celestial bodies
- ships, planes, and aircraft
- words signifying parts of letters (e.g., Dear John)
- specific software programs

The names of months, days of the week, and holidays are considered proper nouns. References to the seasons and numbers of days of the month are not considered proper nouns.

Every spring, Victoria Day falls on a Monday in May.

The meeting is held on the second Tuesday, of January, June, and December.

Capitalize the names of school subjects only if they are languages; however, capitalize the names of specific courses.

| CAPITALIZING NOUNS | |
|---|---|
| **COMMON NOUNS** | **PROPER NOUNS** |
| a god | Zeus |
| a book | Book of Mormon |
| a city | Kamloops |
| a man | Marcel |
| my aunt | Aunt Agnes |
| a language | Portuguese |
| a movement | Romanticism |
| a political party | New Democratic Party |
| a planet | Mars |
| a ship | *Queen Elizabeth II* |
| glass container | Kemmerer bottle |
| a software program | Microsoft Word |

In his final year, he will need to take microbiology, chemistry, biology, English, and Spanish.

Professor Woodman teaches Mechanics of Materials to all students in the engineering school.

## TITLES WITH PROPER NAMES

Capitalize the title of a person when it is part of a proper name.

Dr. John Tuzo Wilson      Rev. Lois M. Wilson

Ron Date, P.Eng.      Douglas Fairbanks Sr.

Judge Shepperd gave his decision on the appeal.

Titles are derived from common nouns indicating a person's status: reverend, doctor, judge, senior, and so on. When such words appear as common nouns, do not capitalize them.

A judge presided over the inquiry.

*Note:* In some cases, if the title of an important public figure is used alone, the first letter can appear as either a capital letter or a lowercase letter. Conventions vary.

> The <u>prime minister</u> [Prime Minister] dodged the protester's pie.

## FIRST WORD OF A SENTENCE

Capitalize the first word of a sentence.

> Estimate subsampling error in at least 10% of the samples being processed by sorting another subsample of equal size.

If a sentence appears within parentheses, capitalize the first word of the sentence. However, do not capitalize the first word if the parentheses are within another sentence.

> The effects of plaque on the heart valves are significant. (<u>See</u> Figure 6.)

> The effects of plaque on the heart valves are significant (<u>see</u> Figure 6).

## FIRST WORD OF A QUOTED SENTENCE

Capitalize the first word of a direct quotation, but do not capitalize it if the quotation is blended into the sentence in which the quotation is introduced.

> Follett concluded the article, arguing, "However, if this is to be the decade for design and innovation, if we are to humanize high tech, we need to first address the issues of language."

> In his article "Eco-tourism Boom: How Much Can Wildlife Take?", Bruce Obee says that "<u>tour</u> boats . . . are a fraction of the traffic."

If you need to interrupt a quoted sentence to include explanatory words, do not capitalize the first word after the interruption.

> "When deciding to contract LIDAR, most people have some concerns," Robert Fowler asserts, "<u>because</u> no legitimized specifications have been written to address this technology."

## FIRST WORD AFTER A COLON

When an independent clause appears after a colon, capitalizing the first word is optional; if the content after the colon is not an independent clause, do not capitalize.

> For the moisture and sieve analysis of sodium chloride, set up the following equipment: balance (0.01 g accuracy); sieves (Canadian Metric Standard square mesh sieves—12.50 mm, 9.00 mm, 5.00 mm, 2.00 mm, 900 mm, 400 mm and 71 mm complete with catch pan); sample splitter; mechanical sieve shaker; containers (metal pie plates, 200 mm diameter); and a drying oven (capable of 110°C).

> Quantitative sampling is difficult: The contagious distribution of benthic macroinvertebrates requires large numbers of samples to achieve reasonable precision in estimating population abundance.

## ◼ ABBREVIATIONS AND ACRONYMS

Abbreviations are more widely used in scientific and technical writing than in writing for the humanities and social sciences. Be consistent in your use of abbreviations. Consult a technical dictionary or online authority for the accepted abbreviation for any term or unit of measurement.

Acronyms are formed from the first letter of each significant word in the name of an organization or the name of a technical process or material: ARRL (American Radio Relay League), FRP (fibreglass reinforced plastic), PPE (personal protective equipment).

## ABBREVIATIONS IN TECHNICAL WRITING

Technical writing abbreviates most units of measurement, names for technical materials, and the names of organizations when appropriate. Here are the rules.

- Abbreviate units of measurement following numerals denoting an exact quantity: 18 psi, 22 μg/l, 34 pfd. Learn and use commonly accepted abbreviations for units of measurement in your professional discipline.
- Write abbreviations in the singular (e.g., 4500 rpm).
- Use lowercase letters for abbreviations except for letters standing for proper nouns or adjectives or those capitalized by convention.

180 psi             2400 Btu             147.060 MHz

- Do not use periods after abbreviations, except when the abbreviation spells a word.
- Do not use signs, or visual symbols, for abbreviations in the text of your document.

16 ft. by 48 ft
The living room wall will measure ~~16' × 48'~~.

Exceptions include conventional use and graphics.

35%             55° north             16' × 28'

Abbreviate names of organizations, as well as technical and nontechnical terms, as long as the first mention gives the full title. Form these abbreviations without periods or spacing. Such abbreviations are called acronyms.

Agricultural Stabilization and Conservation Service (ASCS)

Coastal Area Management Act (CAMA)

aquifer storage and recovery (ASR)

science, technology, engineering, and mathematics education (STEM)

## ABBREVIATIONS IN GENERAL WRITING

### TITLES WITH PROPER NAMES
Abbreviate titles and degrees immediately before and after proper names.
   Do not abbreviate a word that can be used as a title or a degree if it does not accompany a proper name.

professor
The ~~prof.~~ gave an inspiring lecture.

Do not use titles and degrees redundantly:

Dr. Steven Edwards, M.D.

Instead, use one of these options:

Dr. Steven Edwards        Steven Edwards, M.D.

## ORGANIZATIONS, CORPORATIONS, AND COUNTRIES

Use standard abbreviations for names of countries, organizations, and corporations.

UK (or U.K.)    FBI    NORAD    RCMP    CIDA    TSN    RCA    IBM

To save money, she got a room at the <u>YWCA</u>.

---

### ABBREVIATED TITLES AND DESIGNATIONS

| BEFORE PROPER NAMES | AFTER PROPER NAMES |
|---|---|
| Rev. R. W. McLean | Edward Zenker, D.V.D. |
| Dr. Wendy Wong | Paul Martin, Jr. |
| Asst. Prof. Tom Simpson | Margaret Barcza, M.B.A. |
| Ms. Germaine Greer | John Bruner, LL.D. |
| Mrs. Sodha Singh | Eleanor Semple, D.D. |
| Mr. Wil Loman | Roy Shoicket, M.D. |
| St. John | Barbara Zapert, Ph.D. |

---

Sometimes, you may want to introduce a less familiar abbreviation into your paper, for example, COMECON for the Council of Mutual Economic Assistance. In that case, do the following:

1. Write the full name of the organization followed by the abbreviation in parentheses.
2. For each subsequent reference to the organization, use the abbreviation on its own.

B.C., A.D., a.m., p.m., no., $

Use the standard abbreviations *B.C., A.D., a.m., p.m., no.,* and $ only with particular years, times, numbers, or amounts.

The abbreviation B.C. (Before Christ) or the acceptable alternative B.C.E. (Before the Common Era) always appears after a specific date.

156 B.C. (or B.C.E.)

The abbreviation A.D. (Anno Domini) or the acceptable alternative C.E. (Common Era) always appears before a specific date.

A.D. (or C.E.) 65

Use *a.m., p.m., no.,* or $ only with a particular figure.

5:15 a.m. (or A.M.)          8:30 p.m. (or P.M.)          $175          no. 16 (or No.)

In formal writing, do not use these abbreviations without particular figures.

*afternoon.*
We arrived for the dance in the early ~~p.m.~~

*number*
We used Chi Square analysis to estimate the ~~no.~~ of salmon in the stream during spawning season.

## LATIN ABBREVIATIONS

Some readers may be unfamiliar with Latin abbreviations, so keep their use to a minimum or use English equivalents.

| ABBREVIATION | LATIN | ENGLISH MEANING |
|---|---|---|
| c. | *circa* | about (in reference to time) |
| cf. | *confer* | compare |
| e.g. | *exempli gratia* | for example |
| et al. | *et alii* | and others |
| etc. | *et cetera* | and the rest |
| i.e. | *id est* | that is |
| N.B. | *nota bene* | note well |
| P.S. | *postscriptum* | postscript |
| vs. | *versus* | versus |

In informal writing, such as personal e-mails, it is acceptable to use Latin abbreviations.

Jennifer wants to go the Canadiens game this Tuesday. It's the Canadiens vs. the Flames. After the game let's grab a burger, etc. N.B. Dominique and her gang will be there.

In formal writing, use the full English words or phrases.

The Sumerians came down to the bank of the Euphrates and
*approximately*
Tigris rivers c. 3500 B.C.E. Many artifacts provide evidence of
*, for example,*
their cultural advancement e.g. the bronze mask portrait of King Sargon and the headdress of Queen Shub-ad.

## MISUSES

Abbreviations are not appropriate in general writing.

*Canadian literature*
Margaret Atwood is a popular author in ~~Can. lit.~~ classes because she has written so many outstanding novels.

| CATEGORY | FORMAL | INFORMAL |
|---|---|---|
| Names of persons | Jennifer | Jen |
| Holidays | Christmas | Xmas |
| Days of the week | Tuesday to Thursday | Tues. to Thurs. |
| Months | from January to August | Jan. to Aug. |
| Provinces and countries | Saskatchewan | Sask. or SK |
| Academic subjects | Biology and English | Bio. and Eng. |
| Units of measurement* | 6 ounces | 6 oz. |
| Addresses | Madison Avenue | Madison Ave. |
| Subdivisions of books | chapter, page | ch., p.** |

 * except metric measurements
** except as part of documentation

Metric abbreviations are often permitted in formal writing, as in 25 *kg* or 15 *mm*. However, do not use a number written in words with an abbreviation, as in *twenty cm*.

Abbreviations are acceptable in company or institution names only if the abbreviation is part of the official name, as in *Jack's Windows & Roofing Co.*, or *Writer's Inc. Consulting*. Never arbitrarily abbreviate a company's name. For example, if a company's name is *Randolph Architectural Group*, do not shorten it to *Randolph Arch. Gr.* When corresponding with any company, use the full name as it appears on the company stationery, in the firm's advertising, or on the company's website.

## NUMBERS FOR QUANTITIES

Technical writing is full of exact, measured quantities: electronic measurements taken in the field, measured amounts of cement and gravel in a concrete mix, and so on. Technical writers therefore tend to use numerals more frequently than do other writers.

- Use numerals for quantities combined with units of measurement (e.g., 500 *rpm*).
- Use Arabic numerals for quantities of 10 or greater. If no other rule applies, write quantities of fewer than 10 in words.

  12 cm            180 kPa            six horses

- Use numerals for all quantities in a series, that is, a list of quantified items in a sentence.

  Drill 10 mm holes on a 45° angle in the footing form; secure the flanges with 30 cm spikes.

- Use numerals for times of the day, days of the month, quantities of money, decimal expressions, and percentages.

  10:20 a.m.        May 18        $45.79        3.14159        63.4%

- Do not begin a sentence with a numeral. Either write out the quantity in words or rewrite the sentence.

  *use*
  ₍ₐ₎10 cm to 15 cm of compacted crushed stone or gravel ~~is used~~ for the base.

- Write approximations or indefinite measurements in words. The language must clearly indicate that an approximation is intended. Use approximations sparingly.

  The concrete pump has a maximum output of about two hundred cubic yards per hour.

- Write large quantities in a form combining numerals and words (e.g., $23.4 *million*).
- In compound number adjectives, write out the first number or the shorter number and use a numeral for the other (e.g., *sixty 15-cm spikes*).

## HYPHENATION

Hyphens are used to form compound words. The technical writer uses many compound expressions for technical concepts and measurements: *sodium hydroxide, boom pump, nonstop operation*, and so on.

Compound terms should be hyphenated in some circumstances, but not in others.

- In general, write prefixes solid with the root word, as in *pre + determined = predetermined*. Note these instances of hyphen use:
  - to permit internal capitalization (e.g., *post-LIDAR* scanning)
  - to aid pronunciation (e.g., *re-allocate*; *re-form*, meaning "to form again")
  - when *self* is used as a prefix (e.g., *self-lubricating bearings*)

- Hyphenate compound adjectives, but do not hyphenate compound nouns.

  sodium-chloride solution, *but* sodium chloride

  flow-chart evaluation, *but* a flow chart

- Hyphenate to avoid ambiguity. Consider *twenty two litre plastic containers.*

  twenty-two litre plastic containers

  twenty two-litre plastic containers

- Never hyphenate a compound formed with an adverb (e.g., *a highly prized safety record*).
- Hyphenate compounds with letters.

  A-frame      I-beam      S-curve

  When uncertain, observe dictionary usage.

# SCIENTIFIC NOTATION

## THE INTERNATIONAL SYSTEM OF UNITS

The international system of units, or SI, is the accepted form of the metric system of measurement. Its use is advocated by the Canadian Standards Association (CSA). SI is also the official system of measurements for Canada. A complete list of units is available from Natural Resources Canada in the *GSC Guide to Authors: The International System of Units.*

## THE USE OF SCIENTIFIC NAMES

Scientific names, also known as, "binomial nomenclature" or "binary nomenclature," is a formal system of naming species which makes use of Latin. The use of the nonliving language Latin removes the possibility of misunderstanding through the natural process of evolution in a living language. Local names in local languages for the same species can vary greatly and cause misidentification; the scientific name universally applied avoids these problems.

Each scientific name consists of two parts: the genus followed by the species within that genus.

At the first occurrence of the common name for a species in your text, note the scientific name. After the first occurrence, you may use the common name alone.

Italicize Latin words used in scientific names. Capitalize the name of the genus, but not the name of the species. In common names, capitalize only proper nouns.

  pine marten (*Martes martes*)

  wood bison (*Bison bison athabascae*)

  American black elder (*Sambucus nigra* subsp. *canadensis*)

In scholarly texts, the scientific name is followed by the abbreviated or full surname of the scientist who first published the classification.

black spruce (*Picea mariana* [Mill-] B.S.P.)

Norway spruce (*Picea abies* [L.] Karst.)

spruce budworm (*Choristoneura fumiferana* [Clem.])

# ◼ MATHEMATICAL EQUATIONS

Leave space between all mathematical equations and the surrounding text. Centre short equations. Begin longer equations flush with the left-hand margin and continue them, if necessary, on the second and successive lines indented two spaces.

Be sure to number equations and formulas in the text by placing a numeral in rounded brackets on the right margin of the line below the equation. Write a reference to the equation into the text: *Equation (3)*, where *3* is the equation number assigned in sequence through the document.

---

THE FORMULA FOR HEAT FLOW UNDER THESE CONDITIONS IS

$$Q = \frac{k(T_1 - T_2)\,At}{d} \qquad (3)$$

where

| | |
|---|---|
| $Q$ | = heat flow, |
| $k$ | = coefficient of thermal conductivity for the refractory material, |
| $T_1 - T_2$ | = temperature drop from hot face to cold face, |
| $A$ | = area of the wall, |
| $t$ | = time, |
| $d$ | = thickness of the wall. |

---

**Chapter 9** • Mechanics

# CSE DOCUMENTATION

The Council of Science Editors (CSE) produces a style manual that is updated regularly. The latest edition is the seventh, titled *Scientific Style and Format: The CSE Manual for Authors, Editors and Publishers* (Reston, VA: Council of Science Editors, 2006). The following is a brief overview of the two systems described in CSE documentation.

- Name-Year: This system is used in biology and the life sciences. The name-year system is based on the notion of linking the author's surname with the date of publication in the citation, and then listing the sources of information alphabetically by author surname in the references list.
- Citation-Sequence: This system is used in the engineering sciences. It is based on the principle of citing each source of information by number in sequence throughout the document and listing the sources by number in the references list.

## CSE NAME-YEAR DOCUMENTATION STYLE

### CSE NAME-YEAR CITATIONS

Immediately following each text passage or graphic presentation paraphrased or directly quoted from a secondary source, write the name of the author(s), a comma, and the year of publication in parentheses (round brackets): (Adams, 2008). Note the following variations:

- two authors: (Adams and Jones, 2008)
- three or more authors: (Adams et al., 2008)
- page reference(s) for source with more than 10 pages: (Adams, 2008: 151)

Write a lead-in for each paraphrased section, using the author's name in the text, followed by the date in parentheses: "Schneider et al. (1992) showed isolation to be an effective tool for vibration control."

## CSE NAME-YEAR REFERENCES LIST

Place the references list at the end of your text. For a report or formal document, begin the list on a separate numbered page. Title it "References" or "References Cited." Include only sources of information that you have cited. Reference entries for sources are single spaced and formatted as hanging indentations so that author names appear alone on the left margin. Arrange the entries in alphabetical order by author surname. Follow the conventional order of information about the source in each reference entry. The bibliographic information required for each entry varies according to the type of source.

The following are examples of typical sources used in technical communication. Note that items within each entry are usually separated by periods.

### BOOK, ONE AUTHOR

Cole GA. 1988. Textbook of limnology, 3rd ed. Prospect Heights, Illinois: Waveland Press. 315 p.

Mandaville SM. 2002. Benthic macroinvertebrates in freshwaters: taxa tolerance values, metrics, and protocols. Dartmouth, N.S.: Soil & Water Conservation Society of Metro Halifax. 54 p.

### JOURNAL ARTICLE, MULTIPLE AUTHORS

Heino J, Muotka T, Paavola R. 2003. Determinants of macroinvertebrate diversity in headwater streams: regional and local influences. Journal of Animal Ecology 72: 425–434.

### EDITED WORK

Wright JF, Sutcliffe DW, Furse MT, editors. 1999. Assessing the biological quality of fresh waters: RIVPACS and other techniques. Freshwater Biological Association, Ambleside, Cumbria, UK. The RIVPACS International Workshop, 16–18 September 1997, Oxford, UK.

### SIGNED ARTICLE IN ENCYCLOPEDIA

Woolacott RM. 1998. Bryozoa (Ectoprocta). In: Knobil E, Neill JD, editors. Encyclopedia of reproduction, vol 1. New York: Academic Press. pp. 439–448.

### SIGNED ARTICLE IN EDITED WORK

Johnson RK, Wiederholm T, Rosenberg DM. 1993. Freshwater biomonitoring using individual organisms, populations, and species assemblages of benthic macroinvertebrates. In: Rosenberg DM, Resh VH, editors. Freshwater biomonitoring and benthic macroinvertebrates. New York: Chapman and Hall. pp. 40–158.

### TECHNICAL REPORT

Bower SM, McGladdery SE. 2003. A scientific review of the potential environmental effects of aquaculture in aquatic ecosystems, Vol 2. Canadian Technical Report. Fisheries and Aquatic Sciences. Vol 2450, viii, 33.

### CONFERENCE PAPER

Burreson EM. 1998. Molecular diagnosis for MSX disease in oysters: applications to life cycle research. In: 2nd International Conference on Shellfish Restoration. November, Hilton Head, South Carolina.

## GOVERNMENT PUBLICATION, NO AUTHOR

European Commission. 2000. Directive 2000/60/EC: establishing a framework for community action in the field of water policy. European Commission PE-CONS 3639/1/100. Rev 1, Luxembourg.

## DOCTORAL THESIS

Grizel H. 1985. Etudes des récentes epizooties de l'huitre plate *Ostrea edulis* L. et de leur impact sur l'ostreciculture bretonne. Thèse de doctorat. Universite des Sciences et Techniques de Languedoc. Montpellier, France.

## TWO PUBLICATIONS BY THE SAME AUTHOR

Van Banning P. 1988. Management strategies to control diseases in the Dutch culture of edible oysters. Am Fish Soc Spec Publ, 18: 243–245.

Van Banning P. 1990. The life cycle of the oyster pathogen *Bonamia ostreae* with a presumptive phase in the ovarian tissue of the European flat oyster, *Ostrea edulis*. Aquaculture 84: 189–192.

## TWO PUBLICATIONS BY THE SAME AUTHOR IN THE SAME YEAR

Van Banning P. 1990a. The life cycle of the oyster pathogen *Bonamia ostreae* with a presumptive phase in the ovarian tissue of the European flat oyster, *Ostrea edulis*. Aquaculture 84: 189–192.

Van Banning P. 1990b. Observations on bonamiasis in the stock of the European flat oyster, *Ostrea edulis*, in the Netherlands, with special reference to the recent developments in Lake Grevelingen. Aquaculture 93: 205–211.

## COMPUTER SOFTWARE

SAS. 1994. JMP—Statistics Made Visual, Version 3.1. SAS Institute Inc, Cary, NC, USA.

## ONLINE JOURNAL ARTICLE

Lozano SJ, Scharold JV, Nalepa TF. 2001. Recent declines in Lake Ontario populations of benthic macroinvertebrates. [serial online]. Can. J. Fish. Aquat. Sci. 3: 518–529. Available from: http://article.pubs.nrc-cnrc.gc.ca/ppv/f98-031.pdf. Accessed 18 July 2008.

## ONLINE REPORT

Cuffney TF, Gurtz ME, Meador MR. 1993. Methods for collecting benthic invertebrate samples as part of the National Water-Quality Assessment Program. U.S. Geological Survey Open-File Report 93-406. [Online document]. Raleigh, North Carolina: USGS. 65 p. Available from: http://www.usgs.gov/nawqa/protocols/OFR-93-406/inv1.html. Accessed 25 Oct 2008.

## WEB PAGE

Holzenthal RW, Blahnik RJ, Prather A. 2008. Trichoptera: caddisflies. [Online]. Tree of Life Web Project. Available from: http://www.tolweb.org/Trichoptera. Accessed 21 Nov 2008.

## E-MAIL

Elliot B. 2008. Benthic macroinvertebrate survey in Maine lagoons. [Personal e-mail]. belliot@flemingc.on.ca. Accessed 15 May 2008.

# CSE CITATION-SEQUENCE

## CSE CITATION-SEQUENCE CITATIONS

At the first text passage or graphic presentation you have borrowed from a secondary source, place an Arabic numeral in parentheses (round brackets) at the end of the borrowed text or at the end of the graphic caption: ". . . because vibration control is essential to the stability of the unit (1)."

By the same token, place (2) after the second cited work, and so on throughout the paper. Once you have assigned the citation numeral, continue to use the same numeral for the same source. For example, if you use your second cited source again at the end of your paper, you would place (2) at the end of the passage or graphic.

## CSE CITATION-SEQUENCE REFERENCES LIST

Place the references list at the end of your text. For a report or formal document, begin the list on a separate numbered page. Give it the title "References" or "References Cited." Include only sources of information that you have cited. Reference entries for sources are single spaced and formatted as hanging indentations so that author names appear alone on the left margin. Each entry begins with the number that you have assigned to it as a citation. Arrange the entries in numerical order.

The information and formatting for sources in the citation-sequence reference list are the same as in the name-year reference list. Only the order of entries is different; in citation-sequence, the order is numerical.

SAMPLE REFERENCE LIST: CSE CITATION-SEQUENCE

**References Cited**

1. Wright J F, Sutcliffe DW, Furse MT, editors. 1999. Assessing the biological quality of fresh waters: RIVPACS and other techniques. Freshwater Biological Association, Ambleside, Cumbria, UK. The RIVPACS International Workshop, 16–18 September 1997, Oxford, UK.

2. Johnson RK, Wiederholm T, Rosenberg DM. 1993. Freshwater biomonitoring using individual organisms, populations, and species assemblages of benthic macroinvertebrates. In: Rosenberg DM, Resh VH, editors. Freshwater Biomonitoring and Benthic Macroinvertebrates. New York: Chapman and Hall. pp. 40–158.

3. Heino J, Muotka T, Paavola R. 2003. Determinants of macroinvertebrate diversity in headwater streams: regional and local influences. Journal of Animal Ecology 72: 425–434.

# CHECKLIST FOR CSE DOCUMENTATION

Before you submit your final draft, have you

- used the appropriate style of documentation for your audience?
- placed a citation after each borrowed text passage and each borrowed graphic presentation in your document?
- included a References Cited list?
- formatted the References Cited list in hanging indentation, single spaced?
- checked that all entries in the References Cited list are complete, correct, and consistent in the order of information?

If using CSE name-year documentation, check to see that you have

- placed your in-text citations—the author's surname and year of publication—in parentheses (round brackets)?
- organized the References Cited list in alphabetical order by author surname?

If using CSE citation-sequence documentation, check to see that you have

- used Arabic numerals in parentheses for your citations: (1), (2), and so on?
- organized the References Cited list in numerical order according to first citation?

# IEEE DOCUMENTATION

The IEEE is the Institute of Electrical and Electronic Engineers. It was formed in 1963 by the merger of the American Institute of Electrical Engineers with the Institute of Radio Engineers. It advances the theory and application of electrical and electronic technology, encourages technical innovation, and supports the needs of members, including the need for a consistent style of documenting sources of information. Its documentation system is similar to CSE citation-sequence.

The *IEEE Standards Style Manual* (2007) includes many specific standards for describing technical work that the technical writer will find useful while composing drafts of a technical document. These specifics include standard signs and symbols for electronic components and circuits, mathematics, quantities used in acoustics, logic circuits, and SI units (the metric system). This manual is available online from the IEEE website in PDF format (http://standards.ieee.org/guides/style/2007_Style_Manual.pdf).

## CITATIONS IN IEEE STYLE

A citation in the text of a document identifies for the reader the source of the information contained in the text passage immediately preceding the citation.

### FORMS FOR CITATIONS

Use Arabic numerals as citations in IEEE style. Assign the numeral 1 to the first source you use, 2 for the second, and so on. Place the numeral in square brackets—for example, [1]—at the end of the text passage to which it refers and on the same line. Do not make the numeral subscript or superscript. Leave a space before the bracketed numeral; for example, "Schmidt has shown broadband RF amplifiers to be effective at VHF frequencies [1]."

Number citations in the order they appear in the text. Each citation corresponds to a numbered reference in the references list at the end of your document. Use the same numeral for all subsequent citations of that source of information.

When your source of information is in print and contains more than 10 pages, provide your reader with exact page references for easier access. Write the number of the reference followed by a colon (:), a letterspace, and the exact page numbers from your source, like this: "Callaghan and Morris have followed Schmidt's practice of biasing the control element with a variable-rate signal [3: 45–46]."

## REPEATED CITATIONS

Once you have assigned a number to a source, use the same number every time you cite that source. If you use a source by Schmidt on page 6 and assign it the number [2], use number [2] again on page 15 when you cite the same Schmidt source.

Write all your bibliographic information about Schmidt into a reference entry labelled with the assigned number [2] in your references list at the end of the document.

## MULTIPLE CITATIONS

When you have combined information from two or more sources into a text passage, you must cite all of them. The preferred method is to use the numeral citation for each like this: ". . . small and portable, making the antenna practical for outdoor tracking in most types of forest cover [2], [3], [8]." It is also acceptable to write [2, 3, 8].

---

**WRITING AND DOCUMENTING**

Document your sources as you work through the stages of the writing process. It will save time and give your paper more accurate documentation.

As you research, note bibliographic information for your sources of information, especially print sources found in the library or in company files, since these sources may be out on loan when you return to find the information needed to document them in your own references list.

As you draft the document, cite the sources for borrowed information, using any simple author-and-title notation that is convenient. Do not use numerals in the first draft because the number sequence for sources may change as you revise and edit, thus creating extra work.

Once you have written the final draft, change the source notations to IEEE citations in sequence.

---

Remember that the citation is only a brief notation to the reader that the specific passage under the reader's nose came from a source other than the author's own knowledge and mode of expression. The citation numeral links the specific text passage in question to an entry in the references list at the end of the document where complete information about the source can be found.

## REFERENCE ENTRIES IN IEEE STYLE

In the IEEE style, there is a numbered list of references at the end of your document. Its title is "References." List your references in numerical order, the order in which they were cited. Do not alphabetize the list by author surname.

## ESSENTIAL FEATURES

The following are the essential features of the IEEE style for a references list. The purpose of these IEEE forms is to identify different types of sources for the reader at a glance. Standards for the industry or legal issues, for example, have entries distinctive from more common book or periodical forms.

- For an entry, list the author's initials before the last name—most other systems place the author's surname first. Use the author's initials only, except where an organization is listed as an author.
- Place the titles of partial publications (e.g., chapter in a book, article in a periodical, conference paper in the proceedings) in quotation marks.
- Place the titles of whole publications (books, periodicals) in italic typefaces.
- Capitalize every important word in the titles of whole publications (books, journals, conferences), but only the first word in titles of partial publications (journal articles, conference papers, book chapters).
- Do not cite or reference unpublished materials.

## PUNCTUATION AND ABBREVIATIONS IN IEEE REFERENCE ENTRIES

Pay special attention to the style of punctuation, especially the use of periods and commas to identify each item of information within the entry. Note the following details:

- Place periods after each item in the reference entry: name of the author (or authors), title of the work, name of the publisher, and so on. Place commas between elements within items in the entry: for example, M.A. thesis, University of Calgary. Place a period at the end of each entry.
- List multiple page numbers as *pp.* instead of writing out the word *pages*. The page numbers refer to the location of the information you borrowed for your paper.
- Abbreviate the names of months to the first three letters, for example, "Jun."
- Use accepted abbreviations for the names of periodicals or write titles out in full.

## FORMAT FOR IEEE REFERENCE ENTRIES

In your references list, introduce each entry with the appropriate numeral designated by the citation sequence from your report. Use hanging indentation format for the single-spaced entry so that the numeral in square brackets at the beginning of the first line sits on the left margin and subsequent lines begin under the first letter of the first word on the first line.

For example:

[1] W. Gladstone. *Multiplexers for Digital Audio Systems.* Englewood Cliffs, NJ: Prentice-Hall, 1998, pp. 235–318.

The following examples of common types of information sources will help you document your sources.

**BOOK WITH ONE AUTHOR**

[1] W. Gladstone. *Multiplexers for Directional Antenna Systems.* Englewood Cliffs, NJ: Prentice-Hall, 1998, pp. 235–318.

**BOOK CHAPTER**

[2] P. Stevenson. "Resonance suppression in electronic transmit/receive switches" in *VHF Wide Area Service Systems*, 3rd ed., vol. 2. W. Wright, Ed. Ontario, California: Longford Publishing, 2006, pp. 34–82.

**ARTICLE IN A JOURNAL**

[3] D. George. "Klystron interference in thermionic emissions." *Journal of Power Emission Technology*, vol..11, pp. 38–43, July 2003.

**ARTICLE IN PUBLISHED CONFERENCE PROCEEDINGS**

[4] N. Pratt and W.P. Thomson. "Digital and analog attitude control for directional antenna arrays." In *Proc. Canadian Space Engineering*, 2004, pp. 291–297.

**UNPUBLISHED PAPER PRESENTED AT A CONFERENCE**

[5] J.R. Larouche, M.T. Markus, and R.R. Taylor. "Engineering parameters for designing field strength instrumentation," presented at 5th Annual Conference on Aerospace Engineering, Dubai, 2006.

**STANDARDS OR PATENTS**

[6] J.I. Corbett. "Power supply regulation in avionics." Canada Patent 344-7194AV, July 9, 2004.

**TECHNICAL REPORT**

[7] I.P. Martini and J.K.P. Kwong. "Geology and ceramic properties of selected shales and clays of Southwestern Ontario." Ontario Geological Survey. Open File Report 5583. 116 pp. 1986.

**WEBSITE**

[8] M.H. Norman and D.P. Riley. "Intermediate frequency amplifiers." Internet: www.loband.ca/if-amp/index.htm. May 31, 2006 [Apr. 5, 2007].

**ONLINE JOURNAL ARTICLE**

[9] D.R. Pridham. (2005, Nov.). "Hybrid manufacture of gated logic circuits." Electronic Systems. [Online]. 23(2), pp. 11–15. Available: www.mtrobertsc.ca/elect/ES-23.html. [Feb. 23, 2007].

**E-MAIL**

[10] D. Luchuk. "Writing for Engineers Conference." [Personal e-mail]. deluch@shaw.net. Available Aug. 30, 2007.

**TECHNICAL MANUAL ONLINE**

[11] B. St-Louis, ed. "Intermagnet Technical Reference Manual." [Online document]. Intermagnet. Available: http://www.intermagnet.org/im_manual.pdf.

# CHECKLIST FOR IEEE DOCUMENTATION

Before you submit your final draft, have you

- ensured that you are using the appropriate style of documentation for your audience?
- placed a citation after each borrowed text passage and each borrowed graphic presentation in your document?
- included a References list?
- formatted the References list in hanging indentation, single spaced?
- checked that all entries in the References list are complete, correct, and consistent in the order of information?
- used Arabic numerals in square brackets for citation: [1], [2], etc.?
- organized the References list in numerical order according to first citation?

# GLOSSARY OF USAGE

The following glossary alphabetically lists some commonly confused words. Refer to it when you need a quick answer about proper word usage.

## HOW CAN THE GLOSSARY OF USAGE HELP YOU?

The glossary will help you to make correct word choices in both your formal and informal writing and speaking. It provides the following information:

- definitions of words
- sample sentences using words correctly in context
- preferred formal usage for academic writing
- commonly confused words (*explicit, implicit*)
- non-standard vocabulary (*ain't*)
- colloquialisms (*flunk*)
- jargon (*finalize*)
- non-inclusive language (*mankind*)
- redundancies (*and . . . etc.*)
- parts of speech for many words
- cross-references to other relevant sections in this resource
- homophones (*night, knight*)
- common abbreviations
- prefixes (*dis-*) and suffixes (*-ness*)

a, an.   Use *a* before a word that begins with a consonant sound, even if the word begins with a vowel. Use *an* before a word that begins with a vowel sound, even if the word begins with a consonant. Words beginning with the letter *h* often present problems. Generally, if the initial *h* sound is hard, use *a*. However, if the initial *h* is silent, use *an*. If the *h* is pronounced, Canadian writers generally use *a* before it.

**accept, except.**   *Accept* is a verb meaning "to receive" or "take to (oneself)." *Except* is rarely a verb; usually, it is a preposition meaning "excluding."

**advice, advise.**   *Advice* is a noun that means "an opinion about what should be done." *Advise* is a verb that means "to offer advice."

**affect, effect.**   *Affect* is a verb that most commonly means "to influence." *Effect* is often a noun meaning "result." *Effect* can also be used as a verb meaning "to bring about or execute."

**aggravate, irritate.**   *Aggravate* is a verb that means "to make worse or more severe." *Irritate*, a verb, means "to make impatient or angry." Note that *aggravate* is often used colloquially to mean *irritate*. Do not substitute *aggravate* for *irritate* in formal writing.

**agree to, agree with.**   *Agree to* means "to consent to." *Agree with* means "to be in accord with."

**all ready, already.**   *All ready* means "completely prepared." *Already* is an adverb that means "before this time, previously, or even now."

**all right, alright.**   *All right* is always written as two words. *Alright* is non-standard English for *all right* and should not be used in formal writing.

**alot, a lot.**   *A lot* is always written as two words. Avoid using *a lot* in formal writing.

**altogether, all together.**   *Altogether* means "completely, entirely." The phrase *all together* means "together in a group."

**a.m., p.m., A.M., P.M.**   Use these abbreviations only with specific times, when numerals are provided: *10 a.m.* or *1 p.m.* Do not use the abbreviations as substitutes for *morning, afternoon*, or *evening*.

**amount, number.**   *Amount* is used to refer to things in bulk or mass. These things cannot be counted. *Number* is used to refer to things that can be counted.

**and/or.**   *And/or* is sometimes used to indicate three possibilities: one, or the other, or both. It is occasionally acceptable in business, technical, or legal writing.

**ante-, anti-.**   *Ante-* is a prefix that means "before, earlier, or in front of." The prefix *anti-* means "against" or "opposed to." Use *anti-* with a hyphen when it is followed by a capital letter (*anti-American*) or a word beginning with i (*anti-intellectual*). Otherwise, consult a dictionary.

**anxious, eager.**   *Anxious* means "nervous," "troubled," or "worried." *Eager* means "looking forward" and is often followed by the preposition *to*. Do not use *anxious* to mean "eager."

**anyone, any one.**   *Anyone* is an indefinite pronoun that means "any person at all." *Anyone* is singular. In *any one*, the pronoun *one* is preceded by the adjective *any*. Here, the two words refer to any person or thing in a group.

**anyplace.**   *Anyplace* is informal for *anywhere*. Do not use *anyplace* in formal writing.

**as.**   Substituting *as* for *because, since*, and *while* may make a sentence vague or ambiguous, resulting in an unclear cause–effect relationship.

**awhile, a while.**   *Awhile* is an adverb. Use the article and noun, *a while*, as the object of a preposition.

**bad, badly.**   *Bad* is an adjective; *badly* is an adverb.

**being as, being that.**   Both *being as* and *being that* are non-standard expressions used in place of the subordinate conjunction *because* or *since*.

**beside, besides.**   *Beside* is a preposition meaning "by the side of" or "near." *Besides* is a preposition meaning "also," "moreover," or "further." *Besides* can also be an adverb in the sense of "in addition."

**between, among.**   Use *between* when referring to relationships involving two people or things. Use *among* when referring to relationships involving more than two people or things.

**can, may.** *Can* means "know how to" or "be able to." *May* means "be allowed to" or "have permission to." The distinction in meaning between *can* and *may* is still made in formal writing. In informal English, *can* is widely used to mean both "be able to" and "be allowed to."

**cite, sight, site.** The verb *cite* means "to quote, especially as an authority." The verb *sight* means to look at; the noun *sight* means "the thing seen." The verb *site* means "to situate something"; the noun *site* means "a particular place."

**coarse, course.** *Coarse* usually means "heavy and rough in texture" or "crude." *Course* means "a line of movement," "a direction taken," "a way, path, or track," "a playing field," or "a series of lessons in a particular subject."

**compare to, compare with.** *Compare to* means "to represent as similar." *Compare with* means "to point out how two persons or things are alike and how they differ."

**complement, compliment.** The verb *complement* means "to reinforce, add to, or complete something." As a noun, *complement* is something that completes. As a verb, *compliment* means "to say something in praise." As a noun, *compliment* means "a remark of praise."

**conscience, conscious.** *Conscience* is a noun meaning "the sense of moral right and wrong." *Conscious* is an adjective that means "aware, or knowing."

**consensus of opinion.** *Consensus* means "general agreement." As a result, the phrase *consensus of opinion* is redundant.

**contact.** *Contact* is often used informally as a verb meaning "to communicate with." In formal writing, use a precise verb, such as e-mail, telephone, or write.

**continual, continuous.** *Continual* means "repeated many times; very frequent." *Continuous* means "without a stop or a break."

**council, counsel.** *Council* is a noun used to describe "a group of people called together to talk things over, or give advice"; it also applies to "a group of people elected by citizens to make up laws." A *councillor* is a member of the council. *Counsel* as a noun means "advice," and as a verb, "to advise." *Counsel* can also mean a lawyer. A *counsellor* is someone who gives advice or guidance.

**criteria, criterion.** *Criteria* are rules for making judgments. *Criteria* is the plural form of *criterion*.

**data, datum.** *Data* are "facts or concepts presented in a form suitable for processing in order to draw conclusions." *Data* is the plural form of *datum*, which in engineering, surveying, and geomatics indicates a reference point from which measurements are made. Increasingly, *data* is used as a singular noun; however, careful writers use it as a plural.

**differ from, differ with.** *Differ from* means "to be unlike." *Differ with* means "to disagree with."

**different from, different than.** In standard English, the preferred form is *different from*; however, *different than* is gaining wider acceptance, especially when *different from* creates an awkward construction.

**discreet, discrete.** *Discreet* means "prudent and tactful in speech and behaviour." *Discrete* means "separate or distinct."

**disinterested, uninterested.** *Disinterested* means "impartial." *Uninterested* means "lacking in interest" or "bored."

**due to.** *Due to* means "caused by" or "owing to." In formal writing, do not use *due to* as a preposition meaning "because of." *Due* is an adjective and must be used to modify a noun—never a verb, adjective, or adverb. *Due to* most commonly introduces an adjective phrase following a form of the verb *to be* to modify the subject of the sentence. Such phrases after a copula verb are called subjective completions. Consider this sentence: "The pipe was faulty due to an improperly welded joint." The *due to* phrase does not logically apply to the pipe and cannot modify the adjective *faulty* for grammatical reasons. The sentence should read: "The fault in the pipe was due to an improperly welded joint."

**each.**   *Each* is singular.

**e.g.**   This Latin abbreviation for *exempli gratia* means "for example." In the text of a formal document, avoid *e.g.*, and use the English translation *for example* or *for instance* instead. Use *e.g.* only within parentheses (round brackets).

**either.**   *Either* is singular.

**emigrate from, immigrate to.**   *Emigrate* means "to leave one's own country or region and settle in another"; it requires the preposition *from*. *Immigrate* means "to enter and permanently settle in another country"; it requires the preposition *to*.

**eminent, immanent, imminent.**   *Eminent* means "distinguished" or "exalted." *Immanent* is an adjective that means "inherent" or "remaining within." *Imminent* is an adjective meaning "likely to happen soon."

**enthused, enthusiastic.**   *Enthused* is an informal term meaning "showing enthusiasm." Use *enthusiastic* instead.

**etc.**   Etc. is an abbreviation that in English means "and other things." Do not use *etc.* to refer to people. In more formal writing, it is preferable to use the expression *and so on* in place of *etc.*

**eventually, ultimately.**   *Eventually* often means "an undefined time in the future." *Ultimately* commonly means "the greatest extreme or furthest extent." *Eventually* and *ultimately* are frequently used interchangeably. It is best to use *eventually* when referring to time and *ultimately* when referring to greatest extent.

**everybody, everyone.**   *Everybody* and *everyone* are both singular.

**everyone, every one.**   *Everyone* is an indefinite pronoun meaning "every person." *Every one* is a pronoun, *one*, modified by an adjective, *every*; the two words mean "each person or thing in a group." *Every one* is frequently followed by *of*.

**except for the fact that.**   Avoid this wordy, awkward construction. Instead, use *except that*.

**explicit, implicit.**   *Explicit* means "clearly expressed or directly stated." *Implicit* means "meant, but not clearly expressed or directly stated."

**farther, further.**   In formal English, *farther* is used for physical distance. *Further* is used to mean "more" or "to a greater extent."

**fewer, less.**   Use *fewer* only to refer to numbers and things that can be counted. Use *less* to refer to collective nouns or things that cannot be counted.

**finalize.**   *Finalize* is a verb meaning "to bring to a conclusion." The word, though often used, is considered jargon by many people. Use a clear, acceptable alternative.

**fun.**   When used as an adjective, *fun* is colloquial; it should be avoided in formal writing.

**get.**   *Get* is a common verb with many slang and colloquial uses. Avoid the following uses of *get*: "to become," "to obtain revenge," "to annoy," and "to elicit an emotional response."

**good, well.**   *Good* is an adjective. *Well* is nearly always an adverb.

**hanged, hung.**   *Hanged* is the past tense and past participle of *hang*, which means "to execute." *Hung* is the past tense and past participle of *hang*, which means "to fasten or be fastened to something."

**hardly.**   Avoid double negative expressions such as *not hardly* or *can't hardly*.

**has got, have got.**   Avoid using *has got* or *have got* when *has* or *have* alone communicate the intended meaning.

**he/she, his/her.**   Use *he or she*, or *his or her* in formal writing.

**hopefully.**   *Hopefully* is an adverb meaning "in a hopeful manner." *Hopefully* can modify a verb, an adjective, or another adverb. In formal writing, do not use *hopefully* as a sentence modifier with the intended meaning "I hope."

**i.e.**   The abbreviation *i.e.* stands for the Latin *id est*, which in English means "that is." In formal writing, use the English equivalent, *that is*.

**if, whether.** Use *if* to express conditions. Use *whether* to express alternatives.

**implement.** As a verb, *implement* means "to carry out." It is often unnecessary and pretentious.

**in, into.** *In* generally indicates a location or condition. *Into* indicates a direction, a movement, or a change in condition.

**individual.** *Individual* is sometimes used as a pretentious substitute for *person*.

**ingenious, ingenuous.** *Ingenious* means "clever" or "skillful." *Ingenuous* means "frank" and "simple."

**in regards to.** *In regards to* confuses two phrases: *in regard to* and *as regards*. Use either one of these alternatives to *in regards to*.

**irregardless.** *Irregardless* is non-standard English. Use *regardless* instead.

**is when, is where.** Do not use *when* or *where* after *is* in definitions.

**it is.** *It is* becomes non-standard when used to mean "there is."

**its, it's.** *Its* is a possessive pronoun. *It's* is a contraction for *it is*.

**kind, kinds.** *Kind* is singular and should not be treated as a plural. *Kinds* is plural.

**kind of, sort of.** *Kind of* and *sort of* are colloquial expressions meaning "rather" or "somewhat." Do not use these colloquialisms in formal writing.

**lead, led.** *Lead* is a soft heavy metal. *Led* is the past tense of the verb *lead*.

**liable.** *Liable* means "legally responsible." Avoid using it to mean "likely."

**licence, license.** In Canadian English, *licence* is a noun meaning "legal permission to do something." *License* is a verb meaning "to permit or authorize."

**lie, lay.** *Lie* means "to recline." An intransitive verb, it does not take a direct object. The principal forms of the verb are *lie*, *lay*, and *lain*. *Lay* means "to put" or "to place." A transitive verb, it requires a direct object. The principal parts of the verb are *lay*, *laid*, and *lain*.

**like, as.** *Like* is a preposition, and it should be followed by a noun or a noun phrase. *As* is a subordinating conjunction, and it should be used to introduce a dependent clause.

**loose, lose.** *Loose* is an adjective meaning "not firmly fastened." *Lose* is a verb meaning "to misplace" or "to be defeated."

**lots, lots of.** *Lots* and *lots of* are colloquial substitutes for *many*, *much*, and *a great deal*. They should not be used in formal writing.

**may of, might of.** *May of* and *might of* are non-standard English for *may have* and *might have*.

**media, medium.** *Media* is the plural of *medium*.

**must of.** See *may of, might of*.

**myself.** *Myself* is a reflexive pronoun. *Myself* can also be an intensive pronoun. Do not use *myself* in place of *I* or *me*.

**neither.** *Neither* is most often singular.

**none.** *None* is usually singular.

**of.** *Of* is a preposition. Do not use it in place of the verb *have* after *could*, *should*, *would*, *may*, *must*, and *might*.

**off of.** Omit *of* from the expression; *off* is sufficient.

**OK, O.K., okay.** All three variations are acceptable in informal writing and speech. However, avoid these colloquial expressions in formal writing and speech.

**parameters.** *Parameter* is a mathematical term that means "a quantity that is constant in a particular calculation or case, but varies in other cases." It is sometimes used as jargon to mean "any limiting or defining element or feature." Avoid such jargon and use precise English instead.

**passed, past.** *Passed* is the past tense of the verb *pass*, which means "to go by." *Past* commonly means "gone by or ended." Never use *past* as a verb.

**Chapter 12 • Glossary of Usage**

**people, persons.**   Use *people* to refer to a group of individuals who are anonymous and uncounted. Generally, use *persons* or *people* when referring to a countable number of individuals.

**percent, per cent, percentage.**   Always use *percent* (also spelled *per cent*) with specific numbers. *Percentage* means "part of" or "portion," and it is used when no number is provided.

**phenomenon, phenomena.**   *Phenomenon* means "a fact, event, or circumstance that can be observed." *Phenomena* is the plural of *phenomenon*.

**plus.**   *Plus* is a non-standard substitute for *and*. Do not use *plus* to join independent clauses.

**practice, practise.**   In Canadian English, *practice* is a noun meaning "an action done several times over to gain a skill." *Practise* is a verb meaning "to do something again and again in order to learn it." In U.S. spelling, both the noun and verb are spelled *practice*.

**principal, principle.**   The noun *principal* means "a chief person" or "a sum of money that has been borrowed or invested." The noun *principle* means "a fact or belief on which other ideas are based." Note, too, that there is an adjective form, *principal*, meaning "main."

**quote, quotation.**   *Quote* is a verb meaning "to repeat the exact words of." *Quotation* is a noun meaning "a passage quoted." Do not use *quote* as a shortened form of *quotation*.

**real, really.**   *Real* is an adjective. Occasionally, in informal speech and writing, it is used as an adverb, but this usage should be avoided in formal writing. *Really* is an adverb. In informal writing and speech, *real* and *really* are used as intensifiers to mean "extremely" or "very"; such usage should be avoided in formal writing and speech.

**reason is because.**   *Reason is because* is a redundant expression. Use *reason is that* instead.

**reason why.**   *Reason why* is a redundant expression. In its place, use either *reason* or *why*.

**relation, relationship.**   *Relation* is used to describe the association between two or more things. *Relationship* is used to describe the association or connection between people.

**set, sit.**   *Set* means "to set in place, position, or put down." It is a transitive verb, requiring a direct object, and its principal parts are *set, set, set*. *Sit* means "to be seated." It is an intransitive verb, not requiring a direct object, and its principal parts are *sit, sat, sat*. *Set* is sometimes a non-standard substitute for *sit*. Avoid this usage in formal writing.

**shall, will.**   *Shall* was once used with the first-person singular and plural as the helping verb with future-tense verbs. In modern usage, *will* has replaced *shall*. The word *shall* is still often used in polite questions and legal documents.

**since.**   *Since* should be used mainly in situations describing time. If there is any chance of confusion, do not use *since* as a substitute for *because*.

**somebody, someone.**   *Somebody* and *someone* are singular.

**something.**   *Something* is singular.

**sometime, some time, sometimes.**   *Sometime* is an adverb meaning "at an indefinite or unstated time." In *some time* the adjective *some* modifies the noun *time*. *Sometimes* is an adverb meaning "at times or now and then."

**stationary, stationery.**   *Stationary* means "not moving." *Stationery* refers to paper and other writing products.

**than, then.**   *Than* is a conjunction used in making comparisons. *Then* is an adverb used to indicate past or future time.

**that, which.**   Most writers use *that* for restrictive clauses and *which* for non-restrictive clauses.

**there, their, they're.**   *There* is an adverb meaning "at or in that place." *There* can also be an expletive, a phrase at the beginning of a clause. *Their* is a possessive pronoun. *They're* is a contraction for *they are*.

**toward, towards.**   Both versions are acceptable; however, *toward* is preferred in Canadian English.

try and.   *Try and* is non-standard English; instead, use *try to.*

unique.   Like *straight, round,* and *complete, unique* is an absolute. There are no degrees of unique-ness. Especially in formal writing, avoid expressions such as *more unique* and *most unique.*

usage, use.   *Usage* refers to conventions, most often of language. *Use* means "to employ." Do not substitute *usage* when *use* is required.

use to, suppose to.   *Use to* and *suppose to* are non-standard for *used to* and *supposed to.*

utilize.   *Utilize* means "to put to use." Often, *use* can be substituted, as *utilize* makes writing sound pretentious.

wait for, wait on.   *Wait for* means "to await." *Wait on* means "to serve." It should not be used as substitute for *wait for.*

weather, whether.   *Weather* is a noun describing "the state of the atmosphere at a given time and place." *Whether* is a conjunction that signals a choice between alternatives.

while.   Do not use *while* as a substitute for "although" or "whereas" if such usage might create ambiguity.

who, which, that.   Use *who,* not *which* to refer to persons. Usually, *that* is used to refer to things; however, *that* may be used to refer to a class or group of people.

who, whom.   *Who* is used for subjects and subject complements. *Whom* is used for objects.

who's, whose.   *Who's* is a contraction for *who is. Whose* is a possessive pronoun.

would of.   *Would of* is non-standard English for *would have.*

you.   Avoid using *you* in an indefinite sentence to mean "anyone."

your, you're.   *Your* is a possessive pronoun. *You're* is a contraction for *you are.*

# CREDITS

This page constitutes an extension of the copyright page. We have made every effort to trace the ownership of all copyrighted material and to secure permission from copyright holders. In the event of any question arising as to the use of any material, we will be pleased to make the necessary corrections in future printings. Thanks are due to the following authors, publishers, and agents for permission to use the material indicated.

**Chapter 1, page 3:** created by Lawrence Gulston

**Chapter 4, page 40:** "Impact of Anthropogenic $CO_2$ on the $CaCO_3$ System in the Oceans," by Richard A. Feely, Christopher L. Sabine, Kitack Lee, Will Berelson, Joanie Kleypas, Victoria J. Fabry, and Frank J. Millero; *Science* 16 July 2004: Vol. 305, no. 5682, pp. 362-366; DOI:10.1126/science.1097329. Available from: http://www.pmel.noaa.gov/pubs/outstand/feel2633/feel2633.shtml
**Page 41:** Source: Figure 1. Map of Nanaimo River Watershed. "Nanaimo Estuary Management Plan, 2008"
**Page 42:** Source: Ontario Ministry of the Environment © Queen's Printer for Ontario, 2007
**Page 42:** Source: U.S. Department of Transportation, Federal Highway Administration—Bridge Technology: Application of Self-Compacting Concrete in Japan, Europe, and the United States
**Page 43:** Source: Portafab Modular Building Systems
**Page 43:** Available from: http://eesof.tm.agilent.com/products/design_flows/signal_integrity/flow_chart.html. Agilent Technologies
**Page 44:** Source: Ministry of Forests and Range, British Columbia

**Chapter 5, page 58:** created by Lawrence Gulston
**Page 60:** Source: J.A. Stroscio and D.M. Eigler, "Atomic and Molecular Manipulation with the Scanning Tunneling Microscope," *Science* 29 November 1991, Vol. 254, no. 5036, pp. 1319-1326

# INDEX